PSYCHIATRY
IN WAR

PSYCHIATRY IN WAR

By EMILIO MIRA, M.D.

FORMERLY PROFESSOR OF PSYCHIATRY AT THE
UNIVERSITY OF BARCELONA. LECTURER IN PSY-
CHOTHERAPY AND MEDICAL PSYCHOLOGY AT THE
UNIVERSITY OF BUENOS AIRES

W · W · NORTON & COMPANY · INC ·

NEW YORK

ACKNOWLEDGMENT

The author is deeply indebted to
DR. JOHN L. SIMON
for his invaluable aid in the preparation
of this manuscript for publication.

PREFACE

SCIENCE must be more than the mere seeking and recording of the truth. Psychiatry must be the objective, logical, and unselfish effort to promote mental health by means of scientific knowledge.

The author, as a psychiatrist, considers himself a fighting unit against mental illness, worry, suffering, and despair. His personal opinion is that psychiatry has not yet attained the social realization of its possibilities, and that it deserves a more prominent role in present-day warfare.

This book attempts to integrate the psychological and the psychiatric points of view on some of the more urgent problems in the management of military men, so that the greatest possible weight of human power may hasten the victory of democracy. Such an ambitious purpose has been only possible because of the kindness of the Salmon Memorial Committee, and the energy of its chairman, Dr. C. Charles Burlingame.

This book about war has been written in an atmosphere of war, while the author was traveling thousands of miles over the American continent. These circumstances may serve to explain the paucity of concrete data and of references which he could only supply from the quiet room of his lost library.

E. Mira

CONTENTS

ILLUSTRATIONS

CHAPTER ONE

WAR AND THE PSYCHIATRIST

MEANING OF WAR

WAR, ACCORDING to the Encyclopaedia Britannica, "is a fight between human societies—in primitive conditions between savage tribes, in the civilised world between states. Its explanation involves the analysis of the terms of this definition and requires the aid of the sciences that treat of its several elements; of biology to account for the fight, of sociology to explain the State, and of the historical sciences to trace the evolution, in connection with that of the State, of armed forces and of the modes of their employment."

It is no wonder that the word psychology and its derivatives are not even mentioned in the preceding definition. The enormous influence of psychological factors in the motivation, incidence, and results of war has only lately been fully recognized. As recently as World War I, it was assumed that fighting forces were merely engaged in a physical or mechanical contest. If psychological factors were acknowledged, they were included under war strategy, the exclusive property of the General Staff. According to this view, technical knowledge plus a given amount of men and materials should lead automatically to victory or to defeat, depending on the corresponding values of the enemy. It was not so long ago that Napoleon remarked: "God is on the side of the big guns."

Present conditions of war differ greatly from those of Napoleon's time. Then, semiprofessional soldiers did the fighting without interference in the affairs of those for whom they fought. Most citizens were unaware of and indifferent to the details of the conflict. So divorced was the population from the combat that civilian morale as such cannot be said to have existed.

Today wars are of vital, immediate concern to all the people of an embattled nation. War has become a total, global event; the struggle is no longer confined to the firing line, but extends into every detail of life. War is no longer waged by professional mercenaries, but is compulsory for all citizens. Besides the combatants, there are armies of spies, secret agents, guerrillas, fifth columnists, etc., who employ invisible and subtle (psychological) weapons.

Hence it is no longer possible to dismiss the role of psychology. On the contrary psychology has become so important that in several of the belligerent countries there are special ministries devoted to it: the so-called ministries of propaganda or information. It would be more appropriate to call them ministries of psychological warfare. Once complete agreement is reached in respect to the advantages of applying psychological concepts to the management of military organization, what is the role to be played by psychiatrists?

Oddly enough, although the psychiatrists were the first to arrive, the psychologists are now in the saddle and the psychiatrists undecided as to their own function. It was amply proved by World War I that psychiatrists should begin a campaign of mental hygiene as soon as war is declared, in order to prevent mental disorders, maladjustment, delinquency, and other mishaps. One may appropriately inquire as to whether or not the psychiatrists are successfully fulfilling their function. I do not believe that their function has been fully appreciated. The military leaders consider that the average man is normal, and consequently belongs to the sphere of normal psychology. In making this assumption, however, they forget that this man is about to be plunged into abnormal situations throughout the war for which his habitual patterns of reaction are inadequate. We could even assert that in the measure in which a war is rashly and fiercely conducted it becomes normal to behave abnormally. We shall return to this point later.

Every man has certain potentialities for developing abnormal reactions which would be considered pathological in peacetime. One of the best commanders of the Spanish Republican Army once said to me: "I think that during war everybody is upset, nervous, jittery, and perhaps slightly crazy. It is no wonder, then, that you do not find an increasing number of insane. You simply lack a normal background for comparison." The task to be performed by the psychiatrist during war increases in importance rather than decreases.

It is not possible to establish artificial boundaries between the duties of the psychologist and the psychiatrist. Each needs the other and must work in the spirit of co-operation. Considering myself as much one as the other, I never bothered which approach to a given problem was superior. Teamwork has proved successful in dealing with human liabilities from a psychosomatic point of view. Why should we renounce it in dealing with such complicated matters as selection of recruits, maintenance of morale, etc.?

Whereas the psychologist is well equipped to measure specific aptitudes, the psychiatrist is far better prepared to estimate the resistance of a given subject to stress. Moreover, to prevent or to detect early exhaustion in an overworked commander is much more important than to make a fair classification of a hundred inductees.

PSYCHOLOGICAL AND PSYCHIATRIC INTERPRETATION OF WAR PHENOMENA

The first step toward grasping the psychic meaning of war was taken by a great man who, not knowing whether to call himself psychologist or psychiatrist, invented a new name—psychoanalyst. Psychoanalysis may well serve to bridge the gap between psychology and psychiatry.

According to Freud war may be regarded either as "a kind of collective neurosis" or as "a tentative arrangement for periodically discharging the excess of repressed libidinous impulses." Both interpretations assume that repression has a double meaning, since it is at the same time source and effect of civilization. To quote Freud: "Conscience is the result of intellectual renunciation." In its turn, however, conscience demands further renunciations, and so a vicious circle is formed which leads mankind to suffer rather than to profit from culture and civilization. Freud writes pessimistically that "our so-called civilization is to blame for a great part of our misery, and we should be much happier if we were to give it up and go back to primitive conditions."

In connection with Freud's views, which I will not attempt to discuss, it is interesting to remember that more than two thousand years ago Plotinus said that "unsatisfied love is transmuted into rage." Both authors would agree that war does not mean the absence but rather the deprivation of love. The outlook, then, is not so bad as it seems.

To the practical psychologist, war is a period in which human life is completely revolutionized. Moral, legal, economic, social, and even material interpersonal relationships are altered in accordance with war necessity. Habits, affections, and credos are shattered.

During war people must repeat the learning processes of childhood in regard to the fundamentals of living. Who are better prepared to teach in this emergency than those who know most about the mechanisms of human learning? The pupils lack the mental plasticity of infancy; they are of varying ages, of varying cultural levels, and are often unwilling to be taught. Resistance, difficulties, and setbacks are only to be expected; hence the concern of the government to find the most efficient teachers and didactic methods for the new art of living at war.

The change is rendered more difficult in democratic countries, especially in those with high living standards. Necessity and despair, according to an old psychological law, push people to fight; self-satisfaction, comfort and luxury make them conservative and pacific. This may explain why France and Holland were so much more rapidly defeated than Greece and Yugoslavia. This law also suggests why the masses of the Axis states, who have been living under adverse circumstances for many years, adapt themselves so readily to war conditions.

The psychiatrist, on the other hand, is predominantly concerned with the study of pathological human reactions, both individual and group. He considers war an abnormal collective reaction which leads to the substitution of the socially advanced forms of behavior by more primitive ones. All the progress of mankind has been won by subordinating force to reason, coercion to freedom, instinct to ethics. No one can feel free until he acquires control over his bodily cravings. Throughout human history, the Right of Force has been slowly replaced by the Force of Right.

In war, compulsion, mechanical strength, and even brutality prevail over persuasion and reason. The same occurs in madness. Consequently psychiatrists, were they mere professional observers, would be disposed to regard war as a national psychosis afflicting the collective mind. They could then sit back and calmly observe both belligerent parties, or could even be transferred from one side to the other, in order better to compare the reactions of the opposing groups, thereby gaining much valuable data.

Psychiatrists, however, are not merely curious observers, but rather citizens who have to perform a more fundamental task. As physicians, their obligation is to alleviate distress. Since war brings untold suffering, they must postpone their drive for research and confine themselves instead to very concrete aims, which we shall discuss in the following pages.

SOCIAL AND BIOLOGICAL ASPECTS

The biologists offer a very simple explanation of war. War, to them, is merely a particular case—albeit a very pitiful one—of the struggle for existence as old and as widespread as life itself. According to the Lamarckian view, the strong animal survives and the weak perishes. But this statement is true only as long as we deal with organisms devoid of intelligence. Nicolai, in his book on the biology of war, denies its validity in man. On that remote day when the strong young warrior knelt down before the aged, weak magician, man became something more than a purely natural organism: he had discovered the realm of values. Even from a purely concrete, practical angle, war under present conditions means survival of the weak—who are excluded from military duties—not of the strong. When Hitler goes to biology for his attempted justification for war as a natural human aim, he proves once more to be on the wrong path.

Nevertheless, we must not forget that man is also a natural animal, who still retains signs of his fierce and cruel ancestry; it is not by chance that we all have canine teeth. Biologists, therefore, can contribute suggestions to secure the physical and physiological sources of energy. The Spanish War proved that through neglect of the latter, even the best war morale may fail. Hence food is subjected to blockade. Here, however, we are not primarily concerned with this aspect and wish merely to emphasize the insufficiency of all biological attempts to explain war from a purely naturalistic approach.

The same inadequacy characterizes all efforts by sociologists to afford religious, economic, or political explanations of war. Since war is a human phenomenon, it cannot be completely understood unless we take into account all the complex factors which integrate human life. Sociologists are still occupied in discussing which one of the different theories of social and political organization can best explain and, if possible, prevent wars. I hope that sociology will improve its prestige in the near future, but I believe it will do so just in the measure that sociology becomes infiltrated by psychology and psychiatry.

THE HUMANISTIC CONCEPTION

We are finally ready to attempt a synthesis. Man has been described as a "perpetually oscillating and unstable synthesis of antinomies." His life is the expression of conflicting forces, and his behavior is the inevitable result. In man, there is always something more than a struggle *for* life; there is also a struggle *within* life. Human beings are not merely in conflict with their surroundings; they are also in conflict with themselves. War is a mode of behavior which alters for each individual the relative proportions of internal and external problems. Therefore, during war, some persons change for the better, others for the worse.

The outstanding generality of war consists in man's deprivation of spiritual and transcendent dimensions, and in his limitation to the most simple, savage, and natural life in which the only goal is to secure survival.

War would mean only evil for mankind, did it not have for its end a better human state. The leaders of all the belligerent nations, consequently, are forced to promise great cultural, economic, and social changes as the reward of victory. People want to know not merely what they are fighting *against* but what they are fighting *for*.

From the humanistic viewpoint, war is a nuclear and crucial event in the history of mankind; an event on which depends the fate of peoples and nations for centuries; an event from which either regressive or progressive changes emerge. The prewar level of life can never be restored.

AIMS OF PSYCHIATRY IN WAR

Psychiatry must develop the maximum of efficiency to achieve the best adjustment of human resources with the least suffering, both in the war zone and in the rear. Various opinions have been expressed recently as to the concrete aims of such a duty. Professor Overholser in the United States, Professor Moreno in Mexico, and Professor Pacheco e Silva in Brazil have described them. I think it advisable to discuss these aims at some length here, since there is no definite agreement about the limits of the task.

Most of the aims of psychiatry in war must be the product of teamwork on the part of the psychiatrists and other professionals, such as psychologists, psychoanalysts, sociologists, military commanders, etc. The avoidance of interference and of overlapping must be carefully considered by each of these categories in order to obtain maximum benefits. The principal tasks to be performed are:

1. Adjustment of the population to the war effort, according to its capacity and mental energy.
2. Mental prophylaxis for the military and civil population throughout the war, to keep their members fitted for their jobs and to prevent mental breakdown.
3. Proper care of those individuals or groups who become mentally ill or exhausted despite preventive measures.
4. Continuous readjustment of mental convalescents to prevent relapses.
5. Maintenance of high war morale.

Let us see how these different goals may be attained and what is the proper role of the psychiatrists in their attainment.

ADJUSTMENT OF THE POPULATION TO WAR

This aim is so ambitious that it cannot be achieved without perfect planning and integration of the work of all the experts responsible for it. A previous analysis of requirements and needs should be made to adjust the human resources to the emergency. Such an analysis is impossible, however, without proper information as to the resources and intentions of the enemy.

To penetrate such a labyrinth is beyond the scope of this book. We shall confine ourselves to the problem of the selection of civilian and military personnel. The slogan, "The right man in the right place," is even more valuable in war than in peace. Nor can there be any doubt that the psychologists must provide the basis for a proper allocation of individuals in all levels of the war machine.

But the psychiatrists, as well, have something to say on this occasion. They must not wait until they are called upon to give advice. Nor should their function be conceived as the purely negative one of determining who should not receive a given war job. Because of their experience in dealing with men as personalities as a whole and because of their peculiar knowledge of typology and characterology, the psychiatrists are best qualified to determine the mental fitness of a given subject and to predict his output and efficiency under conditions of stress.

On the other hand, there is no sharp boundary line between the normal and abnormal aspects of a given subject. Everyone has in himself both potentialities. It is a question of threshold, rather than of quality or essence, that causes the individual to behave properly or improperly. Therefore, intimate collaboration between psychologist and psychiatrist should lead to better prognostication than the work of either alone. The first could measure the capacities, aptitudes, and vocational abilities of the subject; the second could estimate his ability to use them. Then the problem of psychopathic maladjustment—despite careful psychological tests—would not arise, for it would not only be possible for the experts to tell what is the best assignment for each applicant, but also to determine when, where, and how long he will be able to perform it.

Psychologists have more interest in the common and superficial trends of the mind. They rank the relative values of the mind's instruments, rather than deal with the puzzling problems of the psycho-bio-social relations under overwhelming life conditions. Psychiatrists, on the other hand, are more interested in the practical and immediate evaluation of individual efficiency when an injurious or noxious influence, either inherited or acquired, disturbs the integration of the mental equipment. The possibilities of compensation, over-compensation, displacement, transference, temporary inhibition, etc., of the reaction patterns must be carefully considered in prognosis.

To summarize, we favor the addition rather than the subtraction of effort. It is not a question as to whether psychologists, classification authorities, and psychiatrists should collaborate: they must collaborate unless time and labor are to be wasted in the selective process.

MENTAL HYGIENE IN WAR

Mental hygiene is another objective for which the morale officers, psychologists, and psychiatrists must meet and work together. Here the latter play the major role. Nothing can affect the morale of a group more adversely than the sight of people becoming insane because of the war. Oddly enough, the average civilian or soldier withstands better the news that one of his acquaintances has been wounded or killed than that he has been interned in a mental hospital. A man is more afraid of losing his mind than his body or even his life. Any mental casualty possesses, especially in wartime, a psychic infecting power.

But the worst results occur when an unbalanced person is not recognized and his delusions are accepted by his group. Because of the increased suggestibility of the majority, such half-mad persons are perhaps more dangerous than the truly psychotic and may be used with great success by fifth columnists. Hence it is important to control and observe, periodically, not only the previously determined psychopathic personalities, but those who have not yet been recognized as such. This is the task of a mental hygiene service, to be carried on at the front as well as in the rear.

We believe that no one will deny the third aim of psychiatry in war—the care of mental casualties, just as in peace. Treatment, however, is somewhat different from that prevailing in normal periods. In a peaceful country one does not observe epidemics of neuroses, collective paranoid states, etc., such as sometimes are presented by war.

In the fourth aim—readjustment and reallocation of cured mental patients—we again encounter the necessity for teamwork with applied psychologists and officers in charge of centers of recuperation. Psychiatrists must assist by estimating the probability of relapse and suggesting the most suitable psychological atmosphere for such patients.

Still more important, perhaps, is the contribution of the psychiatrist to the attainment of the fifth aim, the maintenance of war morale. Before we come to the concrete analysis of this aim, however, we must have a picture of the prominent features that characterize life in wartime from the standpoint of a dynamic psychology.

IMMEDIATE AND REMOTE EFFECTS OF WAR ON LIFE

There are as many kinds of wars as there are kinds of people involved. Difference of origin, race, culture, temperament, intelligence, social and economic position are responsible for varying attitudes. We shall attempt what must be a rather abstract and formal survey of the field, since it cannot be denied that, when drafted together, the poor will not react as the rich, the young and healthy as the old and ailing, the fortunate as the miserable.

Nevertheless, for every citizen war implies a change of duties and of rights, a dislocation of prospects and a break of habits, affections, and beliefs. Therefore, we shall attempt to describe some of the most important differences between peacetime and wartime modes of life.

Broadly speaking, in peacetime interpersonal relations take place in a frame of confidence, gentleness, and friendship; whereas in wartime they are tinged with reluctance and harshness. In time of peace a normal man is rarely angry and still less often afraid. In time of war, on the other hand, it is a luxury to be calm and good-humored. Wartime existence presupposes a psychological regression toward the primitive conditions of emotional life that prevailed during early childhood, when the negative attitudes of fear and rage predominate over the positive ones of sympathy and love.

This regression stems principally from the fact that war not merely deprives the individual of his usual comfort and enjoyment, but breaks with the past and requires the rapid creation of new habits. At the same time, it puts the subject face to face with the unknown, preventing him from planning the future. No one knows, on arising in the morning, what will happen to him before nightfall: he may be deprived of liberty or property, transferred to another city, wounded, killed, or, even, unable to return to the same bed as last night. In spite of uncertainty—the most frightful and depressing factor—he must carry on and continue to perform his duty as if danger were nonexistent. Still more, he must appear enthusiastic about the future, smile and conceal his inner doubts and fears.

People are thus plunged into a dangerous, difficult, puzzling, and unlimited present. They are deprived of the support of previous reserves, and they are unable to plan new conquests. What is worse, they are deprived of freedom and of personal initiative. Because in wartime all that is not prohibited tends to become obligatory, there is a progressive absorption of the individual by the war machine. No wonder that the increasing expenditure of mental energy puts the average citizen into a state of nervousness and causes him to react harshly, as he loses his spontaneous affability. The loss of personal freedom is, of course, even more noticeable among the soldiers, since they are attached to their respective army units.

THE ALL-OR-NONE LAW

Because of the sudden change of the frame of reference and of the evanescence of the basic, external supports for mental activity, every individual speculates considerably at the beginning of his new life, only to reach the same blind alley concerning his future. Finally he ceases to attempt it, and abandons himself to the spontaneous, natural, and irrational (affective) mode of life which ruled during the primitive phases of man's evolution. He meekly obeys orders, without trying to absorb them; or, on the contrary, struggles wildly against his environment. People living under war conditions are exposed to abrupt emotional shocks and become more suggestible in consequence. Their behavior becomes unpredictable. They obey the all-or-none law that characterizes the most simple forms of life: the organism either remains insensible and unaffected by the stimuli, or else reacts in the strongest possible way.

One of the most difficult problems arises. Those who are charged with the instruction of the new recruits find the average one to be either apathetic and inhibited or nervous and excited. Since these men suffer from an increase of emotional tone, strong moods are created which restrain their thinking. It is well known that emotional states tinge with their peculiar feeling-tone all levels of the intellectual activities of the individual during a long period. When the individual is frightened, his thoughts are fearful; no matter about what he thinks, his conclusions will be pessimistic. Pavlov's school explains this fact by saying that the basic emotions, being bound up with life or death situations, have the greatest power of irradiation over the brain field, and so exclude the possibility of voluntary change through insight.

For military purposes, it is advisable to discover the specific, individual fears, hates, and loves of each soldier. Soldiers must attain complete mastery over their basic emotions. They must harbor anger against the enemy but not against their superiors; must carefully avoid certain dangers while they seek out others; must feel warmth and friendship toward their companions yet ever be alert to detect treason among them.

Still worse, soldiers must be ready to obey blindly the most unusual commands from their superiors while simultaneously possessing initiative, determination, and insight in the performance. As one of the foremost Spanish Republican militiamen brilliantly summarized the situation: "Officers must be crazy. They ask us now to behave like savages, half an hour later like civilized people, two hours later like beasts, and still later like refined human beings. It takes a long time to become such a mental acrobat and I am afraid of losing my mind in the process of learning it."

DISSOCIATION OF BEING AND APPEARANCE

Another important aspect of the social readjustment in war is the sudden change in prestige and power of many men. Often as the result of haphazard events people become national heroes or objects of general abhorrence. The humble shoemaker becomes superior to the officious proprietor; the elevator boy, now a flight corporal, dictates orders to the businessman who once discharged him. One never knows who is inside a uniform, nor can one predict how he will behave. All one knows is that he has more or less commanding power.

People must be judged by their appearance, and not by their personal value. This peculiar dissociation of being and appearance increases the difficulty of psychological adjustment in wartime.

Nevertheless, the average man possesses an incredible mental plasticity and can overcome all these obstacles provided that he becomes absolutely convinced of the necessity to do so. To obtain this conviction is not easy. If dull, a man may not understand the "whys" of such demands upon him; if bright, he may present dozens of "buts." Hence an enormous amount of information about the war must be supplied and discussions of war philosophy stimulated, covering all angles of the various ideologies. In all citizens of the nation, regardless of their political and religious opinions, the belief must be created that there is no choice but to fight. They must be in the frame of mind to *make,* not merely to *support,* war.

If this goal is attained, people will wish to enter into rather than escape from the warlike spirit. To produce the necessary conviction requires the teamwork of the best brains in the country, especially those best equipped in psychology, psychiatry, sociology, philosophy, ethics, law, and even politics.

REMOTE EFFECTS OF WAR

When war has been waged for several years and the end is not in sight, another danger threatens. People become disinterested, tired, apathetic, and depressed. Nothing matters to them any more, and they behave as if they were drowsy. Neither good nor bad news affects those who crave only rest and peace.

We observed such a state at the end of the Spanish War, when the Munich Pact had removed the only hope of external aid, a hope that hitherto had enabled the Republicans to withstand the deprivation of food, ammunition, sleep, and the loss of their homes. During the months that followed October, 1938, even a streetcar accident in the streets of Barcelona was insufficient to revive the instincts of curiosity and partnership, otherwise so strong among the Catalans.

What was more impressive, the victims themselves did not care, nor did they call for help even though seriously injured.

When such a state of stupor (the French have called it *n'importe-qu'isme* which could be translated by the neologism "don't careism") has been reached, the war is really over. It does not matter whether the stupor is observed at the rear or at the front. Wherever it appears, it means the end of fighting, since there is no possibility for the army to continue if the rear collapses, nor can the rear resist when the army has been destroyed.

Before this disaster occurs, of course, many signs warn of its approach. Strong psychotherapeutic measures can be applied to prevent it. We shall discuss these at the end of the book. Here we discuss the most important obstacle to overcome at the beginning of a war: fear. Many countries have succumbed without fighting, although undoubtedly opposed to the invaders, because collective fears paralyzed their people and leaders. Many errors in the beginning of the war may be avoided if fear can be controlled by the new soldiers. Accordingly, we shall devote the next chapter to the analysis of this basic emotion and to the methods of preventing its deleterious effects among individuals and groups.

CHAPTER TWO

FEAR

FEAR AND ITS MEANING

LET US suppose that a whole population is imbued with the desire to destroy its enemy. In spite of its determination and enthusiasm, as soon as the physical effects of the fighting become perceptible (explosions of heavy bombs, sight of dead and wounded, etc.), almost everyone feels a change inside himself. Fear has made its appearance, and it will not entirely disappear until peace returns.

To paraphrase the Bible: "In the beginning God created fear." Biology confirms that even the simplest living organisms, such as the protozoans, possess not only the property of being stirred up by appropriate environmental changes (irritability) but also that of being paralyzed partially or wholly, temporarily or permanently, when submitted to the alternate noxious action of disturbing stimulation. I believe this property, which I term inactivity, is as important as irritability. The phenomenon of apparent death, already developed in asteroids, and the "immobilizing passive defense" reflex observed in many animals when confronted by human beings are expressions of this property.

Pavlov, after submitting higher mammals to the action of several noxious situations, concluded that "at the basis of normal fear (timidity or cowardice) and in particular of the pathological fears (*phobias*), there lies a predominance of the physiological process of inhibition." If we consider that inhibition implies the cessation of the elapsing motion, we may say that, from the humble ameba to man, the same biological law prevails: according to this law life requires certain conditions of continuity and balance in order to flow. Outside of these conditions life tends to disappear.

Consciously, we experience this inactivating process as a dysphoric state of increasing incapacity, inefficiency, uncertainty, and insecurity. The consequent loss of our reactive power is bound up with a feeling of contraction and impoverishment of the ego. Simultaneously with the aggravation of this conscious experience, uneasiness spreads through all levels of the mind and the individual experiences the onset of the inhibitory process in the form of an increasing sensation of helplessness. The prodigious strength of this primary mechanism of supposed defense of life against death consists, after all, in the partial foretaste of the experience of dying.

Contrary to the statement of classical psychology that fear arises from the idea of danger or from the feeling of threat of injury to the ego, I think that danger, whether subjective (imaginary) or objective (real), is not the cause or even the motive of fear. On the contrary, fear is engendered by the lack of a suitable reaction, in other words, by the loss of fluidity and continuity of the natural reactive course, which secures the discharge into the final common paths of all the potentials excited by internal or external stimulation.

The necessity for securing the elastic spring of the streaming process is so great that fear may arise even without pretense of justification whenever the inertia of the process decreases or is exhausted. This occurs, for example, when the unchaining sign of a planned action fails to appear, so that the desired effect does not occur. Illustrations of this fact in the field of pathology are the "expectation neuroses" (*Erwartungsneurose; neurose d'atteinte*) and the intensive panphobia experienced by cases suffering from a vital depression (Kurt Schneider).

More simply, the unforeseen is more dreadful than the certain and immediate. The knowledge of what will occur is less terrifying than ignorance or doubt. Men frequently feel more hopeless and miserable when unsure of their fate than when death is a certainty. As Anibal Ponce said, doubt is the root of anxiety.

It may appear that this concept conflicts with that formerly defended by Darwin, and more recently by Walter B. Cannon, as to the utilitarian significance, in a teleologic sense, of the fear reaction.

Cannon considers that the fear emotion results from an abnormal
excitation of the sympathetic nervous system which assists in fight
or flight. His investigations of the two "sympathins"—one of which
is supposed to exert an inhibitory action—more closely coincide with
Pavlov's concepts. Yet when Cannon depicts as synonymous the
somatic changes underlying fear, rage, pain, and hunger, I am inclined to attribute his results to an unfortunate selection of experimental animals. From dogs and cats a blend of fear, rage, and pain
is obtained, and there is no possibility of obtaining the pure response
of inactivation. To arouse pure fear, rather than to obtain an "emotional cocktail," it would have been preferable to fling the animals
from an airplane and to examine them immediately upon their land-
ing with parachutes. Then, perhaps, a passive defense reflex, as described by Pavlov, would have been obtained.

PSYCHOGENESIS OF FEAR

The psychogenesis of fear has been the object of numerous recent
works, of which we shall cite only a few.

Sabatier states that fear is the effect of helplessness and incapacity
in the face of life: *"L'homme jeté nu et désarmé sur la planète à peine
refroidie marchant en tremblant sur un sol qu'il sentait encore trem-
bler sous ses pas . . . connut un état de misère et de détresse qui
remplit son coeur d'une épouvante infinie."*

Levy-Bruhl's opinion is that fear was once aroused in human be-
ings, together with superstition, by the "mystery of the unknown."
*"Attrait et horreur, adoration et crainte se donnent ensemble. . . .
"La peur fut d'abord une angoisse diffuse, émotion du mystère."*

According to Rignano's view fear would be the result of emotion
serving the obscure and primary purpose of each organism to sub-
sist in a fixed manner in its physiological state *"tendence de l'être à
perseverer dans son être, tendence a l'invariance."*

Lacroze believes that fear arises from the fight between a tendency
to immutability and a tendency to vital prospection: *"Une vie qui*

est essentiellement mouvement et progrès, des individus qui en sont les aspects figés et arrêtés . . . telle est l'opposition fondamentale d'où nait l'angoisse."

Christin's and Meyerson's views concur in considering the self as the real source of fear. The former says: *"L'angoisse est la peur de soi-même";* the latter states: *"L'angoisse est surtout la peur du mystère que tout homme porte en soi."*

Brissaud asserts that fear and anguish are a "cogitation of death."

Janet writes: *"L'angoisse est une émotion avortée, un processus affectif arrêté ou dévié dans son cours. L'angoisse se rapproche de la peur qui est la plus élémentaire des émotions. De la même façon que l'action dégénère en agitation, l'émotion dégénère en angoisse."*

Freud supports the view that fear is a morbid element which sometimes accompanies the defensive reactions. Its origin proceeds from the suffering inherent to the action of birth. His disciple, Reik, dwells upon the fact that fear of life *precedes* fear of death and that the former—being implicit in the so-called conservative instinct—is nothing but a conditioned reflex of the latter. On his own account, Jones, another disciple of Freud, believes in the existence of an insufficiency of libidinal gratification in the deep levels of all fears; he concurs with the popular belief that courage is the companion of probity, but this differs from clinical tests in many instances.

Wallon holds the criterion of the existence of a certain opposition between the light and intense degrees of fear, since while the first are of external origin, the second are due to a "weakening of the postural tone."

Similar in a way is Devaux's and Logre's opinion when they state that anguish represents *"le fait affectif original"* and that its cause is to be found in the *"structure psychobiologique de l'animal."*

Those scholars who have made direct observations on patients suffering the effects of frightening situations supply us with no less a variety of opinions. Schilder regards "the expectation of some harm" as the cause of fear when the organism tends to avoid rather than to combat the danger.

K. Goldstein emphasizes that anxiety does not refer, generally, to any concrete object (*"Der Angst ist gegenstandlos"*) but rises, as we assert, whenever the performance of the constitutionally determined functions of the organism becomes impossible.

W. Stern asserts: "The source from which fear emerges is a disgusting impression of unsteadiness and of hesitancy (inconclusion in the future) with life and the world."

In spite of their undeniable variety, these definitions emphasize the fact, already verified by Gardiner Murphy for all emotional reactions, that it is much easier to discuss the effects of fear than its causes, since these do not take origin, as was hitherto generally believed, in the idea of danger, but rather just the opposite; the idea of danger springs from the experience of the effects of fear. In his paper, "Feeling and Emotion," Murphy asserts: "The theory of emotion is a matter of organic function or correlation and causation *within* the organism, not between it and the external realm or course of behavior." Hence the real problem of fear lies *within the organism*. As a candid pupil replied to his teacher's question—"Are you afraid of my question?"—"No, sir, I am afraid of not knowing the answer."

TERRIFYING SITUATIONS DURING THE SPANISH WAR

All wars are terrible, but the Spanish War was among the worst, because it was not merely a war of invasion, but at the same time a civil war and a revolution. Sometimes an individual was far more afraid of a member of his family living in the same room than of the bombs of the enemy planes overhead. I will not describe the countless situations in which the fear emotion was experienced or observed by me at its climax. One single sample may demonstrate how tremendously tragic was life in those days. At the Madrid front, the rebels employed a number of Asturian miners to begin dangerous attacks against our trench lines before the Hospital Clínico. These had been taken prisoners, after fighting on the Republican side, when the Northern front collapsed. They were forced to face the peril of death from all directions; behind them were their real enemies, ready to shoot them at any moment; ahead were their friends, who nevertheless must shoot them too; below their feet a mined field was exploding; in the air above, shrapnel from both sides and airplane bombs completed the ring of death. Sometimes they were lucky enough to plunge into a large shell hole and wait until nightfall in order to reach our trenches. Those who survived came to us in a pitiful state. They presented excellent clinical material for research on the evolution of the fear emotion, whose description follows.

EVOLUTIONARY STAGES OF FEAR

On the basis of my experience as well as that of others, I concluded that it is helpful to differentiate several stages in the evolution of fear. These stages, according to the theory of Hughlings Jackson, correspond to different phases of functional disintegration of the higher brain centers. Kretschmer would interpret them as stages of the "accommodating regression."

Of course, one should not expect to observe all of the stages in succession in a given subject. Constitutional peculiarities, the degree of exhaustion, previous determination (the so-called affective constellation), the time and severity of the fearful situation, etc., may modify in a given case the rigidity of our abstract description. But, allowing for these exceptions, I think it is possible to differentiate six stages of fear, each capable of introspective as well as of objective description.

1. *Prudence and Self-Restraint.*—Observed from without, the subject appears modest, prudent, and unpretending. By means of voluntary self-restraint, he limits his aims and ambitions, and renounces all those pleasures which entail risk or exposure. The individual in this stage is already under the inhibitory influence of fear. He reacts with a prophylactic avoidance of the approaching situation.

Introspectively, the subject is not yet conscious of being afraid. On the contrary, he is rather self-satisfied and proud because he considers himself endowed with greater foresight than other human beings.

2. *Concentration and Caution.*—In the second stage, the subject has already entered the field of the fearful situations, but still controls his responses. His movements evince his cautious attitude: they are no longer spontaneous, now that they are submitted to a more severe control of attentive self-criticism, but are slower, more accurate, and more meticulous. The voluntary self-restraint is aimed to secure the basic and immediate purpose toward which all the available energy is directed. The subject overreacts in order not only to attain but to assure success; he wastes energy in the superfluous effort. A tendency to repeat and review movements, the so-called iteration, may also be observed.

Subjectively, the victim is worried and preoccupied; he reinforces his attention as well as his interest in the performance. Doubt as to his efficiency is already present and easily changes into apprehension of failure. A small cloud of pessimism invades his spirit; to overcome it, he attempts to rally all his courage. To the external world he still successfully pretends to be calm, confident, and reserved.

3. *Apprehension and Alarm.*—In the third stage, the patient is objectively frightened. His attitude is one of worry and distrust. Superfluous movements make their appearance; secondary and insignificant actions are magnified; hesitations are manifest, together with oscillations and alterations in rhythm and precision of the essentially required movements.

Because of the immoderate narrowness of attention, the subject's consciousness is restricted. Praxic failures which increase the lack of control are observed. A tendency to withdrawal of the extremities with sudden tremors may also be noted.

Subjectively, the preoccupation, already existing in the previous stage, is magnified so that it effects a division of the stream of consciousness. The flow of thought is affected. The ideation is disrupted, and thought loses its clarity. The ego experiences increasing unsteadiness and insufficiency. In the measure that the subject is convinced of his inefficiency, the helplessness of the ego increases. Silly actions are attempted and may be stopped before their conclusion. Confusion of movements results, and the subject approaches the next stage, in which he will lose completely the control of his behavior.

4. *Anxiety or Anguish.*—In the fourth stage, the subject's behavior loses functional and purposeful unity. New actions are attempted before the conclusion of the preceding; the psychomotor pattern is disorganized. The increasing excitation of subcortical and mesencephalic centers is responsible for a continuous expenditure of pointless movements, some of which are insistently repeated. The subject accordingly resembles an automaton, although he is still aware and can make conscious verbal responses.

A tendency to discharge in the neurovegetative sphere the impulses that have been driven back by the barrage of the effectors gives rise to the so-called visceral storm. The anarchy present at the conscious level spreads to the internal organs as well. In this stage the diencephalon begins to take command over the cortex, which is not yet completely inhibited. Conflicting waves and counterwaves meet the higher and subcortical centers, and dissociated movements, stereotyped gestures, and dysmetric actions are observed externally. Trembling and spasms are also noticeable.

Subjectively, suffering reaches a climax in this stage. The subject experiences an extremely unpleasant sensation of losing his mental balance; he claims that he can no longer control himself. Occasionally he may react with desperation and attempt the destruction of himself or of his immediate surroundings. In so doing, he does not experience any particular feeling of hate or rage; he is merely the spectator, not the author of his impulses.

At other times, the conscious self appears completely dissociated from the effector arc of the nervous system. The subject may deny that he is moving and claim that he is calm and obedient to orders, at the same time as he is committing nonsensical acts.

5. *Panic.*—Previously, the subject was on the brink of complete loss of consciousness. Now his behavior is directed from the thalamic and

mesencephalic centers. Movements of the utmost violence are observed. These cannot be restrained, either consciously by the victim
or externally by change of situation or reassuring measures. The final
motor storm has begun that sometimes gives rise to fits, at other times
to catastrophic "deflexes." The subject may run—whether forward or
backward is a matter of chance. Nothing can stop him, and three
or four persons are needed to hold him even if he is normally
weak.

There is no wonder that people in the stage of panic on the battlefield can perform deeds which may later be described as heroic. In
fact, when "escaping ahead" in a twilight state, soldiers may conquer
positions and rouse the courage of their comrades who are unaware
of the basis of such actions.

Subjectively, the panic stage is experienced as a nightmare, consisting of a peculiar, irregular stream of delirious, oneiric, distorted
mental images, most of which are forgotten when the subject returns
to normal. The so-called subconscious or deep personality (Kraus)
may record the perceptions during this stage, so that hypnotic treatment is required to recall the experiences in this state.

6. *Terror.*—When the sixth stage is reached, it becomes impossible
to distinguish between objective and subjective aspects. Inhibition has
reached all the encephalic levels and has stopped the automatic reactions that were at their climax during the preceding phase.

There is, perhaps, the possibility that sufficient postural tone may
be retained to enable the victim to stand; or, perhaps, he lies in a
bizarre posture on the floor. No matter how he is placed, he remains
motionless as a stone. He is, in fact, petrified or apparently dead.
His pallor and lack of expression reveal complete exhaustion of psychic life. The return to the earth—and I assume that the word "terror" is derived from "terra" rather than from "tremor"—has been
completed. Such inactivation may even be permanent. This occurs
when inhibition spreads to the vital centers of the medulla oblongata.
I have observed two cases of death without injury in soldiers who

were submitted to prolonged fright when exhausted. Cannon explains such deaths by a process of dehydration, decrease of blood volume, and colloidal precipitation.

When recovering from the final stage, the victim begins to open his eyes, although he still lies like a rag doll. He must be handled very carefully, since he may suddenly enter the preceding stage of panic with its blind aggressiveness. At other times, recovery proceeds slowly to normal, with somewhat depressive symptoms: the subject may remain for days devoid of initiative—apathetic, lazy, and amazingly unconcerned.

PHOBOGENIC FACTORS

Phobogenic factors include the influences that generate or aggravate fear. There is no doubt that some individuals are born more fearful than others. The fear reaction immediately after birth, as studied by Watson's techniques, gives insight into the strength of the inactivating processes in a given human organism. I do not believe there is a definite relation between the peculiarities of physical constitution and the amount of fearfulness. There is, of course, a direct relationship between the amount of vital energy, health, and strength of the individual on the one hand and his resistance to inactivation by fear on the other.

There is also a definite relationship between the awareness of a danger and the onset of the fear reaction. This correspondence, however, should not be exaggerated, since the resulting fear depends more upon what the subject thinks about the situation than upon the objective peril. For instance, inexperienced soldiers who were terrified during a practically harmless artillery bombardment enjoyed a drive in a motorcar under conditions of great physical danger.

As we saw previously, we are more frightened by our imagination than by our perception of danger. Similarly, an unexpected event, though it be perfectly harmless, entails more fear than an anticipatedly painful situation. One of my colleagues of the medical faculty, courageous in sports, almost fainted when the chairman of the Athletics Committee, a practical joker, used a false hand (a cotton-filled glove) in a congratulatory handshake with him.

In addition to the above, let us now consider the most important influences favoring the spread of the fear reaction in civilian or combatant groups. They are:

1. *Absence of Leadership.*—One vivid experience of the Spanish War furnishes a good example of this. In March, 1938, the Aragon front broke and many infantry units collapsed with the cry, *"Salvese quien pueda!"* ("Every man for himself!") Groups of soldiers in the worst moral and physical conditions were escaping along the road to Lerida. A few dozen officers, however, who rushed from that city, easily succeeded in stopping the flight and reorganizing the men into new units, capable of fighting with refreshed courage.

Men are unable to behave as members of a group unless there is an organized social structure. A number of soldiers deprived of leadership become a mob of anarchic elements unless special training has been given, so that each soldier has very concrete instructions to follow.

2. *Physical and Mental Exhaustion.*—Lack of food, sleep, clothing, and other physical necessities, as well as excess mental work, may lead to such a diminution of the available energies of the individual that he becomes afraid even without logical grounds. We may note another illustrative incident from the Spanish War. The Fifth and the Tenth Army Corps were counted among the best of the Republican Army. These forces bravely supported for several weeks the full weight of the battle along the Ebro River. After almost continuous lack of rest, sleep, and food, however, they were unable to withstand a weaker offensive of the rebels (November, 1938) whereas the East Army, which had rested for some months, resisted successfully.

3. *Abnormal Intensities of Sensory Stimulation.*—Excess of light and noise may make the subject fearful, as well as darkness, silence, or solitude. Of course individual differences are observable here: some

men have specific, peculiar sources of fear. The majority, however, are most frightened by the combination of darkness, solitude, and silence periodically interrupted by unusual or unidentifiable noises.

4. *Unpredictability of the Danger.*—The rapid change of location and the irregular appearance and disappearance of a fearful stimulus increase its deleterious action. We all know how as small an animal as a mosquito disturbs one who, at night, is subjected to its unexpected dives.

5. *Belief in Enemy Encirclement.*—During the previously mentioned offensive in March, 1938, the rebels successfully used small groups of trained Alpinists, who at a given moment hoisted their flags on the peaks of the surrounding mountains. Panic resulted among many Republican patrols, who believed that they had been encircled by the enemy.

6. *Mysteriousness of the Situation.*—Any new weapon is credited in advance with being more dangerous and deadly than a familiar one. Thus the German experts advocated to the rebels a simple ruse for crossing one of the Ebro tributaries. On a windy day the latter spread from their side clouds of strange-colored smoke. This mysterious event was followed by the flight of our soldiers, who did not realize that they were being tricked, but suspected that a new and terrible poison gas was being employed.

7. *Lack of Definite Plan of Action.*—Since fear is a paralyzing emotion, its victim cannot be expected to create a suitable solution to his situation. The most that can be hoped is that he may retain his habitual responses. Whenever concrete instructions have not been previously rehearsed, the probability is that the individual will plunge into the advanced stages of fear through lack of purposeful action.

A clear example may be found in the abnormal fear reactions exhibited in bombarded Spanish cities by soldiers on leave. During an air raid, these men, steeled to much more dangerous conditions at the front, did not know how to behave and could not even find the air-raid shelters. As a result, they were much more afraid in the streets than in the firing line.

REASSURING FACTORS

There is no doubt that fear is diminished when the subject (*a*) feels himself supported by a present, visible group; (*b*) hopes for help, rescue, or revenge; (*c*) is properly protected from a direct hit; (*d*) knows the location of the menacing danger, and the means by which it may injure him; (*e*) has normal awareness and physical strength; (*f*) has a definite objective after overcoming the fearful situation; (*g*) is confident of the efficacy of his own defensive techniques.

If we were to choose the most significant factors, I think that emphasis should be placed upon the harmful influence of lack of prospects and the beneficial effect of determination to achieve a highly desired objective. This is the reason I venture to propose the following:

RULES FOR THE PREVENTION OF UNCONTROLLED FEAR

1. Let the people know the truth about events. It is not possible to publish all the facts, but lies from official sources must be avoided.

2. Give the people sufficient information about what they stand to win if victorious or to lose if defeated.

3. Allow sufficient food, clothing, and rest for those who are face to face with danger.

4. Discuss widely and intensively all objections, doubts, and comments about the situation, until everyone understands the necessity for prosecuting the war.

5. Make the people love the cause for which they are fighting more deeply than the life they lived in the past.

6. Let the people see that everyone shares the same fate, with no special privileges of any kind.

7. Place in authority those who have shown in practice their aptitudes for leadership. Do not rely exclusively on knowledge; place emphasis on efficiency.

8. Prepare rapid and certain means of reassurance and restoration

of confidence for those who begin to falter. Permit them the freedom of unburdening their feelings without suspicion of cowardice or treason. To effect this, provide for every group a trained technician fitted for psychotherapeutic work at the proper moment.

PSYCHOTHERAPY OF FEAR

We have concluded that fear, subjectively considered, is nothing more than the consciousness of individual dereliction, the foretaste of failure, or the prospect of defeat. Hence, the psychotherapy of fear must consist in reassuring the subject as to his own values and potentialities. Much more important than the removal of the frightening object or situation is the obtention of self-confidence. Only when the subject is freed of internal conflicts and reaches a complete agreement within himself, only when he experiences a perfect synthesis of beliefs and purposes does he feel in possession of all his habitual means of reaction and even become able to create new ones in an emergency. In other words, the psychotherapist must develop first the conditions for the individual's internal adjustment, and second the scheme of life most suitable for his personal resources.

When the subject likes what he has to do, when he has faith and enthusiasm in his aims, when he fights for some beloved goal—then the inactivating influence of fear will be almost insignificant, regardless of the objective danger. The most timid girl becomes the most courageous mother when compelled to rescue her child from the attacks of an enemy; neither flames nor bullets will hinder her defense of so dear an object. When a person is in love, he becomes transformed and effused. He no longer lives within his body, but rather within the object of his love. Whereas fear implies infusion (introversion) and abrogation, love supposes plenitude and ecstasy; this is why the antidote of fear is not courage, but love. To be a hero means to be under the sign of Eros, the god of love.

It is impossible to bring anyone from an attitude of fear to one of love unless he first reaches the intermediate stage of the firm maintenance of a being. Only those who feel steady are capable of transcending and of doing. The greatest desire and the greatest aim of love is creation, in order to reach eternity. Hence Supreme Love is also called the Creator.

Religion has, and will have, so tremendous a force because it promotes faith in eternity. We can understand why the Christian martyrs were not dismayed when they faced the tortures in the Roman circus. They were all in ecstasy—outside of the boundaries of their bodies. To summarize: only those who believe have the determination to perform; only those who have an aim will overcome obstacles, ignore dangers, and resist adversity.

Fear reactions must be overcome by scientific education—social, medical, pedagogical, and psychological. Faith must not be exposed to changes of mood; beliefs must not be left to chance. Both must be rooted in a frame of physical and mental health, in a broad, realistic view of the world. Man must know *who* he is, *where* he is, and *what* he is called upon to do; in addition, he must know *why* he has duties to perform and pleasures to enjoy. Only when these philosophical premises have been scientifically fulfilled does a person achieve a personality; then, and only then, will he be something more than a human animal. Even the most cruel and ferocious beasts may be made to flee through fear; but the defenders of Madrid, of Guadalcanal, and Stalingrad did not suffer from fear, because they were proud of and faithful to their historic duties.

Let us hope that, in the world to come, social psychotherapy will obtain the goal that everyone take the same pride in the performance of his social duties as the best defenders of democracy do now.

TECHNIQUES OF RECONDITIONING IN WAR PHOBIAS

It has been shown by the experience of the Spanish War, and also by that of the present war, that some persons present very peculiar and specific forms of irrational fear, whereas they behave normally under conditions of stress. Thus, for example, some people are more afraid of the air-raid signals than of the bombs themselves. One Spanish officer became anxious whenever he saw a small group of soldiers near headquarters, because he had the absurd idea that these soldiers might be enemy spies disguised as Republicans. Psychoanalysis has dealt successfully with all these phobias, but war psychiatry has no time to lose in a search for remote causes. The military psychiatrist is called upon to readapt these men quickly and effectively; he is not asked why they are ill or how he cures them.

I strongly favor dealing with all these cases in a personal and dynamic manner. A combination of persuasion and suggestion must be immediately followed by experimental reconditioning, i. e., by inducing the patients to learn and to perform the proper response in the specifically phobogenic situation, artificially provoked by the experimenter. As soon as the patient can bring forth the proper behavior response under experimental conditions, he is called upon to repeat it by facing, voluntarily, the actual situation, under the distant control of the therapist.

Later we shall expand this technique (see Chapters Six and Seven), but this preliminary sketch had to be advanced here, since many cases of war fears are referable to individually conditioned fear experiences, where psychological roots are to be found in the patient's earlier life rather than in the present situation. A very clever essay on these clinical forms from the psychoanalytic point of view has been written by Glover in his booklet, *The Psychology of Fear and Courage,* but I very much doubt that the simple information regarding the mechanisms underlying such phobias would prove effective in suppressing their effects.

CHAPTER THREE

ANGER

THE ANGER REACTION AND ITS ORIGIN

THE BIOLOGICAL source of anger is, like fear, a general property of living matter. Cells and organisms are irritable and, when stimulated by certain exciting physicochemical agents, deliver an amount of their own energy, sometimes considerably greater than that of the stimulus.

To this basic phenomenon we must add a psychological factor in order to understand the anger reaction of higher animals including man. This factor is the partial stopping of the flowing streams of action. As soon as the subject becomes aware of something that may bring about a failure of his hopes and plans, he experiences anger against it. Psychologically considered, anger implies the previous experience of a threat to the individual's freedom of thought or action. This is also the condition for the origin of a fear reaction.

Fear and anger become united in zoological evolution. If fear is too intense, anger cannot spread, whereas when anger dominates, fear is almost unnoticeable. Only in very extreme and rare situations, however, do we have a pure emotion of fear or a pure emotion of rage. Even in war, vital situations are not sufficiently noxious as to overwhelm and menace the individual's life to such an extent that he becomes totally terrified. So, during war, we meet peculiar blendings of fear and rage, instead of either in pure form.

BLENDINGS OF FEAR AND RAGE

Let us watch this commander as he faces a bad turn in battle. His movements and commands are emphatic and assertive. He is too impatient: he wants every soldier to obey with lightning rapidity. He shouts, threatens, insults, and offends those who are trying to carry out his orders. Is it not obvious that this man is suffering from the infiltration of his fear, and, in order to counteract its effects, is trying to emphasize his power of command? In the measure that he is losing authority he develops authoritativeness. Apparent anger masks internal fear.

We can also imagine the opposite situation: the offended servant is afraid of the consequences of rebellion and conceals his rage. He appears to be pale and trembling, whereas actually he is exploding within, because he would like to spring upon and kill his offending superior. In both cases we have a blending of fear and rage; in the first, the anger is apparent and the fear repressed; in the second the reverse is true.

On the other hand, these blendings are almost always tinged with anxiety (see Chapter Two). Whenever the corresponding offensive and defensive patterns of reaction fail in the attainment of their goals, we may observe increasing feelings of despair and mistrust. The subject then becomes more dangerous, until he reaches a critical point at which his anxiety is discharged, either against the external world, in the form of indiscriminate aggression, or against himself, in the form of suicidal attempts. In fact, we have observed soldiers who, in a fit of "temper," sometimes committed acts of rebellion, at other times attempted desertion, and finally shot themselves.

FACTORS DETERMINING AGGRESSIVENESS
AND FIGHTING POWER

The relative proportion in which fear and anger may blend on any given occasion depends on several factors, among which we must emphasize (a) constitutional aggressiveness of the subject; (b) individual power of self-control; (c) previous affective disposition; (d) amount of self-love or narcissism; (e) immediacy in time and space of the hated object; (f) supposed strength or aggressive power of the object; (g) previous experience regarding the probability of victory or defeat, in the event of a showdown; and (h) personal advantages of facing or escaping the hated object.

Only when all these factors combine to impel the subject toward the destruction of the source of his anger is this emotion experienced maximally—i. e., as fury. Otherwise, it may be repressed, transmuted, or projected into abnormal forms of reaction. I shall now describe three of these forms, since it is most important to prevent them in wartime.

The human mind is too complicated to justify any attempt to deal with it in as schematic a manner as the pioneers of animal psychology formerly did. Complexity, however, is not a sufficient excuse for renouncing any attempt to classify the anger reactions of wartime.

1. *Displaced Anger.*—This form, also known as transferred or projected anger, occurs frequently. It appears early in wartime and consists in substituting for the hated object another one less difficult to overcome. Thus, for instance, the Germans are now displacing their hate from the military to the civilian zones in the occupied territories because they feel themselves frustrated in their fight against the Allied armies.

Another example of displaced anger is to be found in the quarrels that sometimes break out between the military authorities and civilians of the same nation. Despite my respect for the armies, I must confess that they all suffer more or less from this kind of reaction at the beginning of a war. Military authorities are excited, impatient, and disposed to be angry and intolerant toward nonmobilized civilians. They dictate drastic war orders, emergency military laws, severe penalties, and Draconian prohibitions, as if the citizens they are to defend were the real enemy. Of course this severity, as of all military codes, may be explained by the necessity for maintaining military prestige and discipline; but it is undeniable that sometimes such measures arouse general alarm among the already troubled population and increase its reluctance and worry.

The civilians, in their turn, have no one upon whom to discharge their nervousness, and, consequently, they project it against the political authorities and the government: "We are making a bad start"; "We have not yet found the proper leaders for this emergency"; "Those who plunged us into the war should be the first to go to the firing line"; "The enemy is not so much to blame as ourselves, because of our lack of preparation." At other times the displacement goes further and citizens rant against "the lack of religious and moral feelings," "human stupidity," and so on.

Of course, when Mr. So-and-So makes such comments, he is very confident of not being contradicted, because neither the "warmongers" nor "human stupidity" can meet him in argument. Accordingly, he speaks freely.

When displacement takes the form of reversing the subject and object of the anger, we speak of projection. Then the subject denies that he feels anger but claims that he is hated by the object of his (projected) anger. We shall deal with this form, because of its psychiatric importance, at the end of the chapter; it is responsible for many persecutory delusions and other severe mental symptoms.

2. *Critical Anger.*—A second type of abnormal—and more dangerous—anger reaction is that which drives the subject to demand "immediate action" to smash the enemy with a "terrible blow" (*"un coup foudroyant,"* as the French say). Such people require a blitzkrieg—to be carried out, of course, by specialized troops; they claim that things are going too slowly, fabricate a dozen short cuts, and daily rush into their superior's office to make complaints, criticisms, suggestions, or illuminating remarks about this or that detail, man, or organization. In doing so, they disregard their own tasks and become a negative factor in warfare. Of course, such individuals stick their noses into others' affairs because they do not like to carry out their own obligations.

3. *Retaliatory Anger.*—A third type of anger reaction, more likely to be observed in civil wars but also arising in all wars, is that motivated by personal revenge. The subject's aim is to exact from the enemy in the measure he feels himself injured. This kind of behavior was frequent among uncultivated peasants at the beginning of the

recent Spanish War. In fact, many literary masterpieces have been devoted to laudatory descriptions of popular avengers, whose atrocities are considered heroic.

It is a matter of opinion whether retaliatory attitudes should be encouraged or repressed in the soldiers. Some experts are in favor of giving them concrete motives of anger, but my personal experiences are rather discouraging in this respect, and I should always prefer the development of a fighting attitude based not on subjective hate but rather on proper information and understanding of the moral grounds for the duties of every citizen. Otherwise, we are encouraging anarchic behavior, except in isolated cases of intelligent people who are to risk all they have, such as spies and guerrillas.

Another point to be emphasized is that war of today involves the forced occupation of some countries not only by enemy but by Allied forces as well. The latter may try to defend the people whose land they invade as a prophylactic measure. The ignorant peasants are not aware of the strategic reasons, however, and are unable to make a distinction as to whether they are to be protected or exploited. Since in both cases they feel themselves dominated, they usually move to the rear, where they infect other zones of the population that have not experienced this unexpected military occupation. I have personally witnessed the disastrous effects of such migrations during our war, and in spite of the fact that the official reports always said that this proved that the people would not bear the enemy's presence, the truth was that they did not like the presence of their allies much better. The practical conclusion of all this is to avoid, as far as possible, sudden movements and encroachments of armed forces upon regions that have not been previously prepared for such visits.

ANGER AND AGGRESSIVENESS

Before we proceed further, let us make clear that there is no direct relation between anger and aggressiveness: a man may fight without eagerness, and, conversely, may display anger without attempting to fight. Only when anger invades the deeper levels of his being and pushes him blindly toward a concrete destructive goal does he come into the state of fury, so that an inseparable unity is formed of the hated object, the anger emotion, the fighting purpose, and the devastating action. This fury, however, being the extreme degree of anger, as terror is the extreme degree of fear, does not leave much room for skill and efficiency. In fact, this so-called thalamic rage is very closely related to the thalamic fear, i. e., the panic reactions, described in Chapter Two. Therefore, military experts are rather reluctant to employ substances and procedures that transform the individual into an automaton—excitants and strong alcoholic beverages. Benzedrine and its derivatives, however, may be advised whenever an individual who has been submitted to strenuous work and emotional duress complains of exhaustion and the clinical examination reveals low blood pressure. On such occasions these preparations may relieve fatigue, but caution must be exerted in their administration late in the day because they tend to interfere with sleep and so may aggravate the insomnia already present in such cases.

RAGE AND ELATION

The most characteristic state of elation is that of mania. In this state the individual feels omnipotent and so tends to adopt a tyrannical attitude toward the environment, although sometimes he also experiences a craving for generosity, cheerfulness, and love. Gross has pointed out that in all hypomanic and manic patients there is an increasing irritability which leads them to suffer from violent outbreaks of rage.

Psychoanalysts explain the manic state as the consequence of the liberation of the ego from the control of the superego. MacCurdy claims that mania and elation are closely related and that both are to be regarded as a regression to the level of puberty, in which the subject, under the influence of new hormonal secretions, experiences a kind of rebirth and develops unlimited ambitions. The truth is that an elated individual is a kind of divinity who considers himself invincible.

Thus, it is always desirable for a commander to send his troops into battle in a state of elation combined with hate. To accomplish this, special addresses are made by the military leaders, who on such occasions have the opportunity to test their powers of leadership. When adept, they choose the proper theme, the proper moment, and the proper gestures and vocal inflections, to combine in an optimal degree persuasion, suggestion, and even compulsion. Then the miracle is realized: "The word is mightier than the sword." Even a small contingent of poorly equipped troops may defeat a powerful foe.

The ability to accomplish such effects is considered by German psychologists to be the fundamental quality of leadership. Thus Adolf Hitler wrote: *"Führer sein ist Massen in Bewegung setzen"* ("To be a leader is to put masses into motion").

When elation predominates, the battle may be regarded by the participant as a competitive game, as on the field of sport. He begins with an attitude of gallant bravery and may even behave as an amateur insisting upon "fair play" toward his opponent. The German psychologists praised this gallantry in preparing the German youth for fighting against the poorly armed troops of their initial enemies. But as soon as the German Army faced an equal, and the fight became deadly serious as it is now, they changed the slogan from "War is adventure" to "War is hell and only demons can survive in it."

We may assert that Americans are still facing their battles with the spirit of gallant bravery, whereas the Germans and Japanese are already fighting with an attitude of tragedy. Sooner or later the present cruelty of the Axis troops will be replaced by a depressing feeling of unconcern and apathetic self-defense, such as is already exhibited by the Italians. Then they will merely fight to avoid punishment, and so their fighting power will approach zero.

DELETERIOUS EFFECTS OF ENVY, JEALOUSY, RESENTMENT, AND REVENGE

One of the most typical forms of emotional blending is to be found in the state of jealousy. Here the subject experiences anger and hatred against someone who possesses something that he desires. A jealous person considers himself frustrated and betrayed; he experiences mistrust and despair; and perhaps he plans revenge. Curiously, however, as soon as he is reassured and cheered, or as soon as he obtains the desired object, he forgets all his resentment and rapidly returns to normal.

Jealousy is frequently observed among troops of different branches, among units of the same branch, or among commanders of the same General Staff. Painful consequences arise, and the effects may even be worse than those of fear. Jealousy implies envy, and the latter is a tremendously self-devastating state, since the victim constantly inflicts upon himself the torture of recalling his frustration. The subject hates the envied person because he considers himself incapable of deserving his place or possessions. Only in the measure that he doubts his own value does he envy others.

When anger is repressed it turns into hate, and when hate is concealed it becomes passive resentment. We shall see in Chapter Five how important this reaction may become in the pathogenesis of military maladjustments. Now I wish merely to emphasize that all these emotional blendings tend toward stagnation, thus depriving the subject of his internal freedom. This is why they are called *passions,* since the subject becomes *passive* in the measure that he cannot react against them.

There are no other means to prevent such states than to develop proper moral guidance by means of psychotherapeutic lectures and informal talks within the army units. These are a real and effective part of the mental hygiene campaign. No one can tell, in fact, how many soldiers and officers might otherwise be victims of their own comrades, since the battlefield offers all possible facilities for killing with impunity.

PERSECUTORY DELUSIONS AS A FORM OF PROJECTED ANGER

During the Spanish War we observed cases of persecutory delusions in so-called normal people as a consequence of the combination of strong hatred with increasing depression. Such cases were especially frequent among the groups of refugees who asked to be enrolled in the army. Since they could not be properly identified, and some had difficulties in adjusting to the new environment, it was frequently observed that they could not establish fraternal relations with the group. Some of them became encysted and resentful. They worried about the fate of their families living in the enemy territory and developed reactive depressions. Some weeks later they complained, for instance, of the presence of spies in the camp: someone had taken a picture of them or had requested their signature to convey to the enemy the information that they were on our side. Hence, their relatives were to be tortured and killed. Once these suspicions began, the victim became afraid of everything.

The remedy was simple. It was necessary to gather all the refugees to form special, homogeneous groups according to geographic origin. Then they became reassured and behaved normally, with no need for additional treatment. The Germans and the British have proved skillful in the handling of the problem of volunteers from the occupied zones.

CHAPTER FOUR

PSYCHIATRY IN THE NAZI ARMY

MEANS OF PSYCHIATRIC SELECTION FOR THE ARMY

IN CHAPTER ONE I insisted upon the necessity for more emphasis upon psychiatric advice in the selection of army personnel, not only of the soldiers, but especially of the officers. Of course, means of selection are numerous and it is best to profit from all, since no single method is an adequate basis for the prediction of efficiency on the battlefield.

The German and the American views differ greatly on these matters. Therefore, despite the fact that Farago and others have given valuable information regarding the Nazi method of selection, I think it may be useful to recall some of the principles of German psychological warfare. I use data from various sources for this purpose:

An article by the Argentine neurologist Dr. Marcos Victoria who lived in Germany as recently as 1940 and secured valuable information on this score.

An article by the Italian psychologist Banissoni.

Private information obtained from interviews with German doctors who were living as refugees in London in 1940.

Some issues of the German journal *Soldatentum* which I found in Buenos Aires.

Private information conveyed by my friend Professor Douglas Fryer which he had collected for his forthcoming book on military psychology.

The chapter on military psychology in Germany in Lopez Ibor's *Las Neurosis de Guerra.*

The principal source of information on the organization of military psychology in Germany is Dr. Max Simoneit's book published in 1938, *Leitgedanken ueber die psychologische Untersuchung des Offizier-Nachwuches in der Wehrmacht.* According to the latter, there is in Germany a central office of the army for "Psychology and Racial Culture." Here the results of several psychological laboratories for the testing of military and naval capabilities are synthesized.

These laboratories, called *Psychologische Pruefstelle,* are manned by two army officers, one psychiatrist, and eight specialized psychologists. The latter are qualified as reserve officers after a long period of theoretical and practical studies and a severe examination (*Referendar der Wehrmachtpsychologie*). Finally they receive the diploma of *Regierungsrat und Heeres, resp. Flieger, Marine-Psychologe* ("Adviser and Psychologist of the Army, Air Forces, or Marines"). In 1939 there were two thousand such psychologists in Germany.

Every year the central laboratory of the Ministry of War concerned with the psychology of defense organizes a special course for psychologists and officers. Two of these courses have been published under the title, *Abhandlungen zur Wehrpsychologie.* In addition, there is a journal, *Soldatentum,* devoted to the psychology of defense, the selection and education of army men. Another collection of six volumes about special work in this field has been published as *Wehrpsychologische Arbeiten,* but the most interesting one, by Major Blau, entitled *Propaganda als Waffe* ("Propaganda as a Weapon"), has not been made available to the public.

All this work is intimately connected with the work of civilian scientists. For instance, in 1934 the General Congress of German Psychologists devoted a special section to military psychology and discussed the new meaning of soldiership (*Soldatentum*) which they finally defined as "the internal attitude which emerges in the strongly vital man in face of a present or future danger, which is reinforced by the struggle against this danger so that it reaches a special autonomy and reveals itself in a particular conception and way of life."

Much more important than the selection of soldiers, is, of course, that of leaders. Simoneit emphasizes that these must possess, above all, a tremendous *Wille zur Macht* ("will to power") with a perfect control over their psychosomatic functions.

The methods of selecting leaders are "totalitarian" (global) and rather indirect. They require the collaboration of psychologists and practical men, the former observing the candidates from the point of view of structural psychology, the latter considering them professionally from a more empirical and characterological angle.

The attempt to ascertain the quality of leadership by means of tests is far from realization. It can only be considered as an experiment in behavior. The method followed is of secondary importance. What counts is the examiner's personality. The examiner should, Simoneit believes, realize the importance of his task and the limitations of his techniques. He should cautiously attempt to exclude personal bias. He must also remember that he can be an indispensable and successful adviser, but that decision must not rest on him alone.

Simoneit offers some hints as to the organization and technique of the examination utilized as well as its fundamental principles. He also states that all those who deny the *Wehrpsychologie* ("psychology of defense") think of it rather in terms of a secret art than of an applied science.

It is advisable to let the candidates and their families know that psychology is the best method for selection, because it does not permit of favoritism and is executed not by cold judges but by professional educators experienced in the detection of psychic, spiritual, and characterological qualities.

The advantages of such a practical conception of psychology are beginning to be observed. How does it define the soldier? What are the properties of a good military leader? How may the empirical and the scientific approaches be combined? These and many other questions are illuminating in attempting to grasp the German point of view.

Let us begin with the meaning of the concept of soldiership (*Soldatentum*). According to the German experts this concept does not mean merely to behave as a soldier under the commands of an officer, but something more. It means to live in a soldierly attitude, to consider oneself an element in the making of the *Grosse Reich,* and

to combine self-denial, meekness, and determination in the fulfillment of military duties. Ziegler says, for instance, that to be a soldier
means to possess a peculiar attitude of devotion to the nation, which
attitude is increased in the event of a national emergency and reinforced by fighting against the danger. There is no special type of
personality better qualified than any other to make a good soldier,
according to the view of Simoneit, Lersch, Lottig, and Kreipe. The
Jaensch brothers, of course, would not agree with this assertion, since
they tried very hard to apply their typology to vocational selection
for the army. In his book, *Korperbau, Wesenart und Rasse* ("Constitution, Temperament and Race"), Walter, the most Nazified of
the Jaensches, asserts that only those belonging to the nordic type
should be chosen as models for the German soldiers. He failed to
realize that neither Hitler nor Göring can possibly be considered as
Nordic types; and it was perhaps because of this miscalculation that
all the work accomplished at the Reichssportfeld in Berlin collapsed
at the end of 1938.

The characteristics of a good leader, according to Simoneit, may
be summarized as follows: He must possess, above all, a tremendous
Wille zur Macht, i. e., will (or ambition) for power, plus the "martial quality." The latter requires (*a*) full control of the psychosomatic
functions involved in the tasks of military command; (*b*) richness of
psychic resources; (*c*) power of suggestion; (*d*) decisiveness; (*e*)
heroic tendency. The last term means the ability to merge all individual ambitions into the attainment of a "pure value" beyond the
limits of personal profit; Scheler calls this "nobility," and according
to Simoneit, it implies self-discipline.

Simoneit analyzes the characters of some of the most outstanding
German commanders—Moltke, Blucher, Yorck, Scharnhorst, and
Gneisenau—and concludes that it would be foolish to expect the
ordinary officer to possess the average of their qualities. In the same
way Scheining asserts that the *Leistungschlabone* ("standard") for
testing the German officers cannot be an abstract one, but should
rather be based on a general view of the professional habits of the

Prussian military tradition, of the demands of the blitzkrieg, and of the ideals of the Nazi theory.

THE GENERAL PRINCIPLES OF PERSONAL SELECTION IN GERMANY

Before describing the techniques of selection, it will be well to emphasize the general principles that are now accepted by the leaders of German military psychology.

1. The first is that of practical knowledge and the scientific psychological approach. According to this principle, practical and scientific observations must combine and coincide in order to be valuable. If the scientific approach has the advantage of greater accuracy, empirical and ingenuous psychological conclusions have the advantage of naturalness, spontaneity, and closer connection with actual mental life. The army psychologists are not to disregard the sources of popular information, but must work co-operatively with the professionals engaged in selecting officers.

2. The principle of globality or wholeness, with its application in the *Ganzheitpsychologie,* rules modern German psychological warfare. According to its theories, conscious life is integrated into a single meaningful whole, which must be approached with a global insight. Of course, a warning must be issued against the tendency to form too quickly a general impression of the personality, and then to use this first impression as a Procrustean bed to which subsequently observed phenomena are fitted. Military psychology must not try to add a list of aptitudes and define the human value of the subject in terms of this sum. The task of the psychologist is to give a fair opinion of men as personalities, rather than to atomize psychological data. The whole being more important than the sum of the parts, the psychological expert must always remember that a special capacity or function is never isolated in the individual, but must be interpreted and evaluated in terms of its integration within the mass of personality traits. Thus, for instance, the reception of telegraphic signals at a

great speed may or may not be considered a good quality for an efficient wire operator, according to the values of the general temperamental tendencies, such as fatigability, endurance of attention, etc.

3. According to the third principle, that of the immediateness of life, psychological understanding (*Einsicht*) depends upon the psychological immediateness and naturalness of the observed reactions, as well as upon the fairness and intelligence of the observer. Hence it is not advisable to bring men into a psychological laboratory, where they would behave in a sophisticated manner; on the contrary, the psychologists must make contact with the applicants in plain, human fashion. The observer and the observed must meet in a normal situation, as informally as possible.

4. The principle of complete observation in the course of testing implies that, whatever is being tested at the moment, the observer must not neglect the opportunity to obtain simultaneous information about the remainder of the individual capacities. For instance, during spirometer tests valuable hints may be obtained concerning the subject's intelligence, whereas the way in which he sits down to solve an intelligence test affords information about his character. The assumption that these traits may be tested later does not justify their neglect at this time.

5. The principle of examining not only aptitudes but also predispositions (*Anlagen*)—although oriented by a basic "racist" criterion in Germany—is a promising one. I personally believe that it brings the psychological and psychiatric examinations closer together, since it demands from the test procedure not only a diagnosis but also a prognosis as to the subject's aptitudes and deficiencies. For this, attention must be turned upon his familial antecedents, his constitutional trends, and his mental conflicts. In this task a trained psychiatrist can and must assist the purely technical examiner.

6. The principle of compensation within the mind's territory assumes that a mind or psychic apparatus possesses not only forces but also volume. Different levels or fields, corresponding or not to neuro-

logical regions, can be distinguished, and each of these possesses what is called a compensating balancing power. When equipped with a powerful and elastic mind, a subject may overcome certain concrete physical or mental liabilities. This is another reason not to over-estimate the results of testing the specific mental abilities.

Another important point of German psychotechnical warfare is the belief that the final efficiency of any soldier is largely influenced by the factor of training. Accordingly, all teaching procedures at the military schools are very carefully controlled by the following methods.

As soon as the German boy enters primary school his military training begins. The idea of submission and sacrifice on behalf of the Reich is constantly developed. At the same time the boy is introduced to a peculiar history of the world, in which Germany is the only decent and lovely country. Soon he joins gymnastic groups where he participates in sports of a military nature. Upon reaching adolescence, he is instructed to believe in every paragraph of the modern German Bible, *Mein Kampf,* and to consider himself called upon to avenge the shame of Versailles. For years it is impressed upon him that Germany is invincible but that all the world is against her except, of course, the Axis partners. The reason for the persecution of Germany lies in the power of three confluent international forces: bolshevism, Jewish capitalism, and decadent imperialist democracy. He learns to hate all these and to trust the only man who can restore German prestige. He also learns how to orient himself in a forest, how to control his nerves when in danger, how to distribute his physical and mental energy. Even on a Sunday excursion, the apparently innocent event is exploited by the teachers to develop strategic knowledge, self-mastery, meekness, and endurance.

German psychology experts have proved that the maximum efficiency of a marching group of persons is reached when they make a short pause half an hour after the start, in order to readjust equipment, and then proceed without knowing the time of the next stop. A proper distribution of "propelling" men is made. These are active members of the Nazi party who are charged with increasing morale. They begin the singing, make jokes, etc., throughout the excursion. Special attention is devoted to develop *Bruderschaft* ("partnership") between the officers and the soldiers during the rest periods. Then all the men mix; and the soldiers are proud of their importance. It is, in fact, significant that in the present *Wehrmacht* the rigidity and severity that were so typical of the Kaiser's time are no longer to be observed.

THE SELECTION OF OFFICERS

In wartime the selection of officers and their promotion to higher rank are, of course, based upon their efficiency on the battlefield. But how was the initial bulk of German officers selected before the war began?

Since an officer must be a leader, a very careful analysis of his character and personality was made before he was allowed to begin training. A team of two selecting officers, a military physician, three psychologists, and, later, one psychiatrist was assigned to each applicant. They proceeded to collect data under the following heads:

1. *Curriculum vitae* of the applicant.
2. Analysis of his expression.
3. Results of psychological tests.
4. Evaluation of the efficiency of his behavior.
5. Final determining examination.

Data of the first category are collected in a rather informal interview. The candidate is asked about memories of his childhood, home life, scholarship, first friendships, personal achievements at different ages, trips, prominent acquaintances, games, books, hobbies, etc. Special importance is devoted to ascertaining how he became aware of the social, political, and economic misfortunes of Germany in the postwar period.

The analysis of expression is divided into (*a*) analysis of mimetism and pantomime; (*b*) analysis of facial and manual gestures; (*c*) analysis of verbal context; and (d) graphological report. The subject is watched during spontaneous conversations with his comrades, arguing and joking. How well is he able to imitate others' expressions? This gives insight into his histrionic and pantomimic aptitudes. Is he cold, rigid, or inhibited when speaking, for instance? As for analysis of facial and manual gestures, ordinary snapshots or photographs are demanded, especially those taken by nonprofessionals. The predominant gestures and postures are recorded. The analysis of verbal context refers not merely to the preferred topics of conversation but also to the mode of constructing sentences (semantic) and the relative proportion of adjectives and nouns, of abstract and concrete judgments, etc., formulated during several spontaneous interviews.

Special emphasis is placed upon the results of graphological analysis. It must be remembered that German graphology, which was developed by Klages and others, has great influence in the German school of psychological warfare. They believe graphology has reached a highly objective stage, whereas graphology in America is practically disregarded.

The psychological testing takes the form of a general examination in which actual concrete problems are presented to the subject, who is allowed to consult books, ask for further information, and solve them in any way he pleases. Once he claims to have found the solution, he is questioned as to how he reached it and about the thinking process that led him to the result. The explanations offered by the candidate, the method used to check his inferences, the hypotheses he made—all this seemingly wasted mental work, viewed retrospectively, gives information as to his general thinking powers, which are much more significant than mere success or failure, since the latter may depend upon extraintellectual factors. His personal opinion about the work he has just accomplished is also requested, and affords a reliable basis for estimating his self-judgment and other trends of character closely related to intellectual efficiency.

As to the fourth aspect—the analysis of the efficiency of the spontaneous behavior—German psychologists are much interested in knowing how many of the purposes of the subject are transformed into successful achievements, how many are dropped without being tried, and how many fail during execution. Such information cannot be obtained unless the examiner is allowed to live very close to the observed and is able to obtain the confidence of the latter.

In order to acquire these data, the examiner may place the candidates in certain experimental situations, which are then considered as "adventures" involving some risk of failure. "Do you think that you can do it?" If the answer is yes, scoring is very simple; if no, further stimulation is required, especially for sporting performances. Manual work is also used, as well as bipersonal competitions, in which the examiner may be one of the partners; no tricks or unfair means are permitted. When the candidate faces strenuous and difficult tasks, the oscillating waves of confidence and discouragement, the retardation and acceleration of movements, the pauses for rest, etc., must be recorded.

Of course, some of the scholastic and professional tasks may serve also for this purpose: how does the officer react when he misses the target on the rifle range; how does he react when praised or criticized by his superiors, etc.?

Now comes the final test: the so-called *Fuehrerprobe* or test of leadership. This last examination takes two days, during which the subject is submitted to interviews, athletic tests, manual and mental performance tests, and—most important—during which he has to command an unfamiliar group of soldiers in certain unpleasant tasks. In this last, the reactions of the soldiers are as carefully registered as those of the future commander, since their reactions are a good index of the ability and appeal of the applicant. At the end, the applicant is confronted with his colleagues to discuss several topics informally with them in the presence of the examiners. No special instructions are delivered, thus permitting the subject to feel at ease. His behavior in the presence of friends is observed.

All the preceding measures are designed to afford a better insight on the part of the examiners into the tested personality. Despite the apparently anarchic way in which the data are gathered, the information is systematized intelligibly and scientifically into the characterological report, which must be complete, objective, and practical.

WORDING OF THE CHARACTEROLOGICAL REPORT

In the elaboration of the report, the following must be observed:

1. The report must contain a first paragraph to orient the reader through the entire report and to facilitate its comprehension. In this paragraph, the predominant quality of the personality of the official under consideration must be pointed out. Sometimes this quality will explain all the other qualities that are pointed out in the course of the report. Sometimes, however, the psychological characteristics of secondary rank disagree with the predominant quality and must be set apart for the sake of objectivity.

2. Together with the predominant quality, the dynamic principle that molds the personality must be pointed out.

3. The body of the report includes a description of the various psychological qualities and the results observable in everyday life and in the special conditions of military life. The examiner should endeavor to remain purely objective and should not produce a literary *feuilleton*.

4. A supplement may be attached in which controversies arising from different observations are discussed.

5. The report will conclude with the diagnosis and prognosis of the personality.

NOTES ON THE GERMAN SELECTION OF FLIERS

If there is any war assignment that can destroy the nervous control of a normal person it is that of piloting a pursuit plane or a dive bomber. Koch and Lottig, Schaltenbrand, Kostitsch, Treutler, Velhagen, Koch, Hartmann, Noltenus, and many others have devoted themselves to the analysis of flying in order to perfect the *Luftwaffe*.

I shall not describe all the careful experiments performed in the William-Kerchkoff Institute of Bad, one among dozens, on the nervous systems and the psychic qualities of pilots. It may, however, be interesting to cite the schema proposed by Koch and Lottig:

SCHEMA FOR THE EXAMINATION OF THE NERVOUS SYSTEMS
OF PILOTS OF THE LUFTWAFFE

	ANIMAL		VEGETATIVE		
	Energy change with the environment		Metabolism		
Somatic	Motility	Sensibility	Digestive tract	Circulation	Respiration
Psychic	Will	Imagination	Euphoria and dysphoria	Emotivity	Tenseness and relaxation
	Spirit (*Geist*)		Mood (*Gemuet*)		

Whereas in normal flying conditions the left part of this schema has control over the right, in altitude flights and in diving the situation is reversed. Special exercises to control the uncontrolled spheres of perception and movement on such occasions are recommended. Some of these exercises are very closely related to the autogenous training of Schultz and the Yoga practices. The capacity to learn such psychosomatic control seems to be greater among well-educated persons. It is an interesting fact that such a well-known Nazi philosopher as Heidegger does not disdain to be a *Luftoffizier*.

CHAPTER FIVE

PSYCHIATRY IN THE SPANISH REPUBLICAN ARMY

THE SPANISH REPUBLICAN POINT OF VIEW

WHEN called upon to review the mental causes of honorable discharge from army service, I maintained the thesis that whereas it was useless to compel a madman, an imbecile, a coward, or even a reluctant soldier to go to the firing line, we ought not to be too generous in discharging all the alleged and presumed mental patients from military obligations. We needed all our men, and besides, once these people believed themselves ensconced in the rear, they might launch dangerous rumors and set up disaffection.

No one, of course, can control what a soldier does with his machine gun under fire; but it is still more difficult to know what he may do with a telephone or a pencil in his home. It was therefore my opinion that whenever a recruit was in possession of his mind at all, he should be used in some manner *within* the army, no matter what his assumed mental trouble. Whenever this mental syndrome deprived him of reason and self-control, naturally he was to be honorably discharged *and sent to a mental institution*. It took time to overcome the resistances to these criteria, but they were finally accepted with very slight modifications. The army classified the enrolled men as being either (*a*) suitable for all services; (*b*) suitable for auxiliary services; (*c*) temporarily discharged; (*d*) permanently discharged; or (*e*) judgment deferred. Let us analyze classes (*d*) and (*b*).

Permanently Discharged.—These men were permanently discharged because they suffered from:

1) Idiocy, imbecility, and chronic mental deterioration (dementia) whenever the clinical antecedents, the observations of their spon-

taneous behavior, and the mental tests coincided to prove that they were unable to understand their military duties or to perform them.

2) Chronic psychoses, especially the so-called endogenous psychoses, in which the symptoms of a mental process, either present or inferable from reliable sources, might be reasonably presumed to be of such a nature as not to permit the subject to adjust to the military regimen. Whenever doubt existed, psychiatric observation in a military unit was required.

3) Epilepsy with severe and frequent fits, with permanent mental defect, or with equivalents verified by observation in a psychiatric clinic of the army.

4) Psychopathic personalities, with a severe and evident hereditary taint, whose reaction tendencies had made them unsuitable for social life and had required previous hospitalization in mental institutions, and whose detection in the observation ward of a military clinic indicated their uselessness for any kind of military duty, either because of the severity of their internal mental suffering or by the chronicity and gravity of their social misbehavior.

Suitable for Auxiliary Services.—These men were transferred to auxiliary services when they suffered from:

1) Mental deficiency, mild forms.

2) Epilepsy when not accompanied by subsequent or alternative mental disturbances.

3) Endogenous psychoses in periods of remission, without mental deterioration.

4) Exogenous psychoses with focal symptomatology, permitting the patient to pursue a vocation.

5) Psychoneuroses and psychopathic maladjustments compatible with vocational achievements.

To clarify the criteria for classification as above, the special instructions that were delivered to all military physicians connected with the induction and assignment of men in the army are transcribed below:

INSTRUCTIONS FOR THE APPLICATION OF THE CAUSES OF UNFITNESS IN THE SPANISH REPUBLICAN ARMY

Theoretically speaking, each soldier must be carefully selected to ensure that his anatomical and physiological constitution is perfect. In practice, it is impossible to attain such perfection since the enormous exigency of men in modern armies makes utopian the attempt to find great masses possessing such perfection. Hence, the requirement of those qualities is limited to special branches of the army, in which they are absolutely essential and for which the number of individuals required is relatively small.

But it is indubitable that the selection must be oriented in accordance with the index of the subject's robustness and his functional capacity, independent of the illness or physical imperfection from which he suffers, without forgetting that there are some illnesses with an absolute value of prohibition because of the immediate danger they imply for the subject or because of the collective social danger through contagion.

Fit for all Services.—This group includes all those persons who possess the standard qualifications of the soldier and those who have some physical defect that does not disqualify them from campaign duty. In short, this group admits individuals with slight physical defects, but not sick men.

Fit for Auxiliary Services.—This group contains in general patients with chronic diseases consistent with the performance of a profession or trade and not contagious, as well as physical imperfections that disqualify from active military campaigns but allow the fulfillment of sedentary functions or military functions of reduced physical requirements.

Totally Unfit.—In general, in this group are included diseases that permanently disqualify an individual from earning a livelihood. From what has been said, it may be inferred that those contained in this third group are declared totally unfit; and their unsuitability must be patent. Consequently, the physician who pronounces such a verdict should not require any effort to prove the justice of it—to point out the individual should suffice.

Those included in the second group, and declared as such to be fit for auxiliary services, do not usually present doubts as to their classification. When the question arises whether a disease is a chronic one or an acute one in the process of healing, decision should be deferred. However, regarding physical defects, it is often difficult to decide whether an individual is fit only for auxiliary services or fit for unlimited services, since there is no sharp boundary between the first and second groups. This may produce in some physicians uneasiness about the equity of the verdict. When this state of doubt arises, it must always be resolved without vacillation, for the welfare of all the services involved.

A necessary condition for the proper fulfillment of the task of the military physician is the recognition of the essential differences between military and civil medical practice. The military physician must often deal with dissimulators and simulators. In peacetime, the dissimulators predominate for obvious reasons; in wartime the other group predominates to the point where there is a very scant percentage of recruits or inductees who do not allege some illness or physical defect. Therefore, the military physician should attach little weight to the subjective symptoms of the examinee but should base his conclusions on purely objective data. Never should the physician interrogate an individual as to specific symptoms unless there is some objective datum that justifies the symptoms of the illness he claims to suffer. The physicians charged with the observation of the supposed unfit should adhere to the same instructions and try to minimize their examinations and special tests, since the latter procedures delay the classification.

For example, if a suspected case of pulmonary disease presents nothing clinically or radiologically, it is unnecessary to examine the sputum, sedimentation rate, or complement fixation. Too many studies obstruct classification and assist simulators considerably.

THE PSYCHIATRIC QUESTIONNAIRE FOR DETECTING POTENTIAL NEUROTICS; SELECTION OF NEW RECRUITS

Until the organization of the psychiatric services, the selection of men in the Spanish Army had been made on the basis of a purely medical examination. Essential as this procedure is, it is usually inadequate to detect nervous or mental disorder, and it is not even intended to provide any information about the recruit's intellectual and temperamental make-up. Any attempt to introduce psychological examination of recruits coming up for assignment was usually opposed on the grounds that they were too disturbed at the time for reliable results and that such testing would involve a loss of time.

Such objections are not valid in relation to the use of group tests such as I used for the selection of some of the Spanish Republican troops. All the men coming to the recruiting centers were gathered in different rooms and asked to fill out the questionnaire reproduced below.

SPANISH REPUBLICAN ARMY

GENERAL INSPECTION OF MILITARY MEDICINE
Psychiatric and Mental Hygiene Services

In order to utilize your ability to the maximum within the Popular Army and to prevent useless hardship and suffering on your part, please answer the following questions with complete honesty.

Given name.........Surname.......Age...Place of Birth.........

Home Address......................Occupation..............

Languages (and dialects) you know...............................

Other training or knowledge (in addition to occupation)...............

....

PLEASE ANSWER THE FOLLOWING QUESTIONS:

1) What is fascism?...

....

2) What are your motives in fighting to exterminate it?..............

....

3) What would our country be like if the fascists succeeded?..........

....

4) What will our country be like after the victory of the antifascists?

....

5) What do you think are your chief duties as a soldier of the Popular Army? ....

6) Where and what type of work in the army do you prefer?..........
....

7) What is your main wish at the present time?.....................
....

8) How would you like to spend your leisure time during your military service?...

9) If you could choose a reward or prize for your services to the Republic, what would you request?..

10) Can you stand fatigue?.......lack of sleep?........cold?........ hunger?........thirst?........

11) Which of these hardships do you think would hurt you most?......
....

12) What physical or other effect do you notice when you are exposed to a fright or shock of any kind?....................................
How do you behave then?..

13) Do you remember any moment in your life when you displayed courage? (Please describe the incident if you care to)..................
....

14) Do you ever faint?...

15) Do you suffer from dizziness?................................

16) How often do you have sexual relations?......................

17) How often would you like to have a 7-day leave if it were possible? Where and how would you spend the time?.........................
....

Other information that might be of value to the army as to your experience and ability:

....
....
....

(If you have not had enough room to answer any question completely, please use the back of this sheet, giving the number of the question you are answering.)

The first five questions on the meaning of fascism, etc., were designed to give some indication of the recruit's level of intelligence by drawing on his ability to deal with fairly abstract relations. The next four questions, concerning desired assignments, present wishes, etc., were intended to discover the interests of the new recruit and his opinion of himself. The next four proved extremely valuable in detecting men likely to suffer from war neurosis.

It was found that these questions offered the subjects who wanted to escape from military duties a good opportunity to realize their desires *by exaggerating their own weaknesses and defects*. All the recruits whose outlook was suspect, as judged from their answers to these questions, were carefully given an individual examination by a trained psychiatrist.

Again, those who gave satisfactory and courageous answers were referred to their officers as capable of rapid training, provided, of course, that the results of their medical examinations were satisfactory. The next two questions were rather confidential, and the last gave a final opening to those with psychopathic tendencies.

To score this questionnaire in the simplest and most practical way, the psychiatrist and his assistants attached to each recruiting center were instructed to rate the answers to the first five questions on a 10-point scale, 5 points indicating the average. In order to make the rating more accurate, some specimens of the most typical answers previously obtained from recruits of different cultural levels were given to the examiners. The answers to most of the remaining questions were rated by a similar method, according to the good faith revealed by the recruits. The rest were merely considered by the examiners in order to see whether further information was required.

Copies of the more important data obtained by this method were sent to the commanders of the units to which the recruits were attached. In their turn the commanders were asked to pass on the information to the medical officers.

Broadly speaking, the cases of mental and neurotic disorders occurring subsequently in the group of approximately twenty thousand troops selected in this way were three times less frequent than among those not given any such examination. This suggests that considerable value would be derived from the adoption of this or similar methods of selection and group testing at the recruiting centers.

REALLOCATION OF MEN ALREADY ENROLLED

The first selection at the recruiting center cannot provide an adequate basis on which to decide in what particular connection a recruit can best be employed. Once he has become a soldier and is tinged with the military outlook, it is possible to examine him more carefully and to suggest for which one of the innumerable occupations in the army he is best suited. There are thousands of men who, after being sorted out in a haphazard way upon enlistment, could be profitably transferred to other sections. There are many others who become ill suited to their jobs through illness or injury. A trained psychologist, fully acquainted with the demands of different types of work and assisted by the advice of a trained psychiatrist, could be of great use in the reallocation of such men to different posts.

In Spain we successfully applied to the different types of military occupation the same classification used by the Institut Psicotecnic of Catalonia in relation to civilian careers, and thus obtained eighteen basic types of work among which it was relatively easy to distribute individuals with the corresponding capacities. (It is to be recalled that the three essential data of this classification refer to (a) the mental and physical capacities, (b) the degree of monotony, and (c) the predominance of perceptual, verbal, or psychomotor responses.)

The factor making a fundamental difference between the military and civilian classification was that of the place of work. In conditions of war it is sometimes more important to determine *where* a subject is to do a job than to decide *what kind* of job he is to perform. For example, cooking is a highly specialized task, but it was found that some of the best civilian cooks failed when sent to the front, the same being true of drivers, barbers, sanitary engineers, and others. Hence it was the duty of the psychologist to choose the occupation, and the duty of the psychiatrist to decide the location of this occupation for the man in question. Thus we see how necessary it becomes to establish teamwork between both kinds of technicians.

INTEGRATION OF PSYCHOTECHNICAL AND PSYCHIATRIC
POINTS OF VIEW IN SELECTING MEN
FOR SPECIAL POSTS

The integration described above becomes still more necessary in selecting men for highly specialized and responsible tasks. Snipers, antitankists, secret agents, etc., were picked from those men who had already shown themselves to be courageous and trustworthy by their previous record in the field. The guerrillas, whose work was to be done in the enemy's field, were especially selected in this way.

The imbrication of the psychotechnical and psychiatric work was, however, greater when the training for such difficult posts was to be made with "new" material, i. e., men who had not yet been submitted to the crucial test of the battlefield. Such men might easily excel in the laboratory-testing and even in the ordinary neuropsychiatric examination but fail as soon they faced the real job in the real situation. Only the trained eye of the psychiatrist, accustomed to look beyond the limits of the explicit verbal and motor behavior and understand the "whole" man, can gather clues for predicting the man's future achievements.

I recall how, when intending to create a psychotechnical device for testing the kinesthetic perception of space in the applicants for an air-pilots' school, I was plunged into research that resulted in the invention of one of the best psychiatric tests, now widely employed in Argentina and Chile. It was a psychiatrist, Rorschach, who discovered all the possibilities of the apparently innocent ink-blot test of Dearborn. Psychiatrists like Freud, Rosanoff, Myers, turning their attention to a psychological device, improve its technique and add to its benefits. I shall not dilate on how the psychopathic reactions of some very intelligent cadets may negate all their technical achievements. In war it is not merely a question of saving lives and machinery; it is also a question of saving fighting time. Whenever a man is discharged from a school or from a particular post after weeks of training, no one can say how far this loss of time could be translated into loss of blood on the battlefield.

GENERAL ORGANIZATION OF THE PSYCHIATRIC AND MENTAL HYGIENE SERVICES IN THE SPANISH REPUBLICAN ARMY

Broadly speaking, we can divide the Spanish War into three periods. The first extended from the outbreak on July 18, 1936, to the repulse of Franco's troops at the gates of Madrid in November of the same year. The second extended from this date to the great rebel offensive in March, 1938. The third lasted from then until the end of the war in March, 1939. During the first stage there was no definite military organization on the Republican side; men going up to the front were called *milicianos* ("militias") and allowed to go and come as they pleased. Hence, no psychiatric services, statistics, or reliable observations exist, though I would venture to state that because of the absence of a real front-line struggle, they probably would not have been very significant.

During the second stage, compulsory conscription was established and the Republican Army created. This improved so rapidly that in March, 1937, it was already able to defeat picked enemy troops at Guadalajara; in July of the same year it won the battles of Brunete and Belchite, and, in December, conquered Teruel. Psychiatric services during this year were spontaneously performed by specialists in different sectors, but were neither co-ordinated with the rest of the medical services nor centralized and supported by an organic criterion.

In February, 1938, I was summoned to organize and control such services. It was apparent that the struggle was a very fierce one, since during 1937 the Republican casualties amounted to over forty-nine thousand killed and two hundred thousand wounded, a high proportion of losses, since the total number of enlisted troops in that period was scarcely eight hundred thousand. (The number of prisoners and missing was, in fact, rather small, but I do not possess the exact figures.)

Some army corps had prepared statistics referring to the incidence of war neurosis and a close examination of them gave the following results:

a) The total percentage of men temporarily discharged because of war neurosis was not more than 1.5 per cent. There were, nevertheless, considerable differences in the personalities of these men and in their rank in the army. For instance, soldiers from the north were more resistant to nervous breakdowns than those from the south, but once the northerners developed a neurosis, recovery was far more difficult.

b) It was striking that the amount of war neurosis observed among front-line troops was slightly smaller than that observed among second-line troops or those at the rear. This could be explained by the fact that the front-line troops (called *ejército de maniobra*) had much better insight into the political situation and the aims of the war than the rest of the army, and, consequently, had higher morale.

c) Anxiety states were rather infrequent, and usually developed into fits before reaching the psychiatric services.

d) The most common form of neurotic disturbance was that usually known as conversion hysteria, especially characterized by paretic, spastic, and dysrhythmic psychomotor symptoms.

In addition to these data, I received invaluable information from Dr. Bermann, an Argentine psychiatrist who had been working in a psychiatric unit at the Madrid front; his experience concerning the difficulties of co-ordination between these services and the rest of the medical organizations of the army spared me much trouble.

With all these things in mind, the Board of Military Psychiatry and Mental Hygiene Services of the Spanish Republican Army was definitely created in April, 1938. A selected staff of thirty-two trained psychiatrists was enrolled in it and distributed among the five battle zones of the Center (Madrid), Extremadura, South, Levante, and East (Catalonia). In each one of these a psychiatric unit was organized, consisting of, first, a psychiatric hospital installed in the rear of the army, more than a hundred miles from the firing line. This hospital had one bed per thousand men served. Second, the unit had attached to it a small number (one to four) of so-called *centros psiquiátricos de pre-frente,* i. e., mobile emergency services of twenty or thirty beds, located at the clearing stations of the evacuating lines of each army corps, fifteen or twenty miles behind the front line. Ordinarily, these services were installed in the vicinity of the campaign hospitals which were, of course, the second step of the whole medical organization, the first being the regimental posts. In all, five psychiatric military clinics and fourteen psychiatric emergency centers were functioning by July, 1938.

The chief psychiatrist and director of these clinics was at the same time responsible for the psychiatric and mental hygiene services in the corresponding military zones. The tasks to be performed in the clinics were, first, to care for all the mental cases sent from the front emergency centers; second, to attend cases coming from the auxiliary troops and services installed in the civilian zone; third, to observe and diagnose the supposed or real mental disturbances exhibited by recruits and considered by the unspecialized physicians of the recruiting centers as being possible causes of military unfitness. Last, but not least, these clinics were in charge of the preparation and equipment of selected officers for the mental hygiene campaign and for the maintenance of the war morale of the army.

A very important fact must now be emphasized—that all the military elements in the rear zone of the army (between the actual front line of the army and the civilian rear) were not evacuated to the central psychiatric clinic but *toward the front emergency center of the corresponding sector* when they exhibited any mental disturbance. They were surprised that instead of going backward they were moved ahead when they complained of mental disorder! The purpose was to avoid the encouragement of malingering or the exaggeration of nervous symptoms as a means of escape from the hardships of military life. The majority of troops in the rear zone of the army were more exposed, even, than those of the front line to the mental contagion of rumors and demoralization emanating from the fifth column. As a matter of fact, that zone constituted a bridge where news from the rear and news from the front mixed and conflicted, so that a tremendous danger of spreading demoralization in both directions arose.

As for the emergency centers at the front, they were in charge of all the men who exhibited disordered behavior in the front zone. These men were evacuated and observed or assisted in these centers for ten days, and then sent back to the front line or transferred to the psychiatric central clinics, depending on the results obtained. Cases of complicated psychosomatic disorders, such as cranial trauma with mental symptoms, severe commotional mental confusions, infectious deliria, and so on, were to be immediately evacuated to the central clinic, whereas the evident psychogenic and hysterical cases were not to be put to bed but treated boldly by suggestive measures and directly transferred to the Centros de Recuperación y Adiestramiento, where much gymnastic and kinetic exercise was the basis of their readjustment. As for the cases of nervous exhaustion in whom evident neurovegetative symptoms and physical weakness were present, they were transferred, for a period not exceeding twenty days, to a rest home or convalescent sanatorium that was connected with the psychiatric clinic and located roughly halfway between this and the front center.

INCIDENCE OF ENDOGENOUS PSYCHOSES IN THE SPANISH REPUBLICAN ARMY

It is well known that cases of endogenous psychosis encountered by military psychiatrists serving in different armies have never been more numerous than those observed among the civilian population during peace. This is true for the dementia praecox and manic-depressive psychoses, although it must be remembered that these psychoses constitute a clear basis for previous exclusion from the army, so that the appearance of a certain number of cases of these types in the troops must be explained either by a delayed manifestation of the *Anlage* or by a precipitating influence of the military life upon their latent disposition.

SPECIAL OBSERVATIONS ON EPILEPSY

As for epilepsy and especially the so-called twilight states and epileptic equivalents of the comitial seizures, I have observed a definite increase in wartime, not only in military but also in civilian psychiatric services. In my university clinic the cases of epileptic psychoses did not fill more than 3 per cent of the occupied beds, whereas in the military psychiatric clinic of Vilaboi they constituted 7 per cent in November, 1938. The probability is that the epileptic form of reaction, more or less implicit in the nervous system of us all, is activated by nervous exhaustion, excesses of drinking, and, perhaps, temporary adrenal insufficiency, which conditions continuously increase in wartime if—as was the case in the Republican Army—neither food nor rest is available to the men.

PSYCHOPATHIC PERSONALITIES AND PSYCHOPATHIC REACTIONS

The new patterns of reactions and modes of existence determined by war conditions (isolation from the family, deprivation of home, change of food and occupation, increase of personal danger, etc.) may alter the psychopathic attitudes, sometimes for the better, sometimes for the worse. In fact, I observed many instances in which schizoid personalities behaved splendidly under conditions of stress, whereas some apparently normal people were plunged into a state of depression or stupor and became rather helpless. In my opinion, no general assertion can be made on this score, since all possible varieties of reaction are observable. Nevertheless, I would say that war life, when not too hard, is more likely to benefit than to aggravate

psychopathic personalities, since it provides a source of stimuli powerful enough to make them forget their own conflicts and feel more
like the rest of the population. On the other hand, it is obvious that
the average citizen becomes disturbed and even a little insane during
war, thus lessening the contrast between him and the psychopath.

Generally speaking, three forms of psychopathic reactions were
observed in the Spanish War. The first was the explosive or agitated
and aggressive discharge. This form had been previously described
by French psychiatrists in World War I. The subject, who was attempting to repress his feelings of fear and disgust, became more
and more introverted and worried; he experienced an increasing
dysphoria which followed him everywhere, until the moment when
his mood discharged either in an hysterical fit or in a crisis of verbal
and motor aggression on the most insignificant pretext. Sometimes
this crisis was followed by a period of apparent amnesia and depression, but at other times it changed slowly into a state of defiance and
negativism. Of course, under such circumstances the individual
violated some of the most serious military rules and was subject to
the death penalty unless it could be proved that all his behavior
sprang from this pathological cause. The antecedents of the individual
were not always illuminating: there were cases with a history of
epileptic predisposition or neurotic trends of character, but many
other cases were of different types of psychopathic personality or
even of hitherto normal people. When such cases were observed, it
was wise to hush up the matter and to make the individual invisible for a while; otherwise military discipline might be seriously
shaken.

A second form of psychopathic reaction—perhaps the most frequent
and most difficult—was drunkenness. The subject felt the need to
get tipsy more and more frequently, until he was unable to perform
any task without the assistance of an alcoholic beverage. The only
possible way to stop the extension of this vice would have been a
prohibition law in the army; but this would not have helped very
much, since the drinking habit was already too deeply rooted in the

average man, and perhaps its victims would have found a worse substitute. Hence the instructions I gave consisted of a special sign on the identification card of all military men who had been found intoxicated, whether or not they had committed any offense. These men were to be closely watched by their immediate superiors and by the regimental physician. The latter began psychotherapy and attempted to discover the motivation of the addiction: Fear? Depression? Worry? Lack of sexual satisfaction? Feelings of guilt? Need to forget? It was found that in a majority of the cases the addicts felt themselves devoid of strength and courage when deprived of their remedy; hence it was not a question of adopting punitive measures, but of aiding them to restore normal feeling tone. For this purpose I recommended, with success, the regular use of a 5 per cent solution of liquor ammoniae anisatus. Also, the groups of drunkards were disbanded and a special partner, previously selected by the physician, was assigned as if by chance to each addict.

All of these measures were insufficient, so I next got in touch with the Department of Medical Information and proposed to begin a scientific campaign to show the evil effects of the alcoholic habit upon those who were most inclined toward it, i. e., the weak and frustrated. A special film was to be projected, showing the different stages of alcoholic intoxication and the corresponding lesions in liver, vessels, and brain. I had great confidence in the value of this kind of propaganda, but our war was coming to its end, and I never had the opportunity to put my opinions to the test.

In recent years, I have developed a very simple and objective test of the psychomotor tension of the individual and have confirmed by means of it that many alcoholics present a constitutional predisposition to depression, justifying their instinctual needs for excitants in the same way as those with temperamental anxiety are fond of narcotics and sedatives. These cases improve rapidly with proper vocational guidance, scientific planning of their psychoneuric expenditures, a certain amount of benzedrine, liver extract, and a rich vitamin diet.

The third form of psychopathic reaction observed in our psychiatric services was that of resentment. Because of the rapid creation of our army, the distribution of ranks was not well ordered; it was mainly a matter of chance who became an officer and who remained a private. Hence, many intelligent and cultivated people were commanded by their mental inferiors. Still worse, some professional officers who remained faithful to the Republic were under the orders of new, improvised, more popular chiefs who suspected them of disaffection. This happened more than once. For instance, the commander of the net of fortifications about Bilbao crossed into the enemy lines on the eve of the fascist attack upon that city; then, of course, a wave of suspicion and distrust descended upon the heads of the loyal officers remaining behind, so that they, in their turn, frequently manifested abnormal reactions. I should venture the opinion that there is no situation more pregnant with mental conflict, more psychotoxic, than that of any man's living away from his social (religious, professional, economic) group in contact with his theoretical enemies. Such a situation is comparable only to that of the enemy aliens now living in the democratic countries, longing for an opportunity to fight against the Axis, but feeling themselves watched and mistrusted.

This reaction of resentment is frequently combined with psychogenic (interpretory) delusions, and is responsible for a progressive isolation (encystment) of the individual who then lives beside rather than within his group. Sometimes he makes himself noticeable by exploding with bitter remarks or caustic criticisms, the more pernicious because they have been cautiously and designedly elaborated.

Fortunately, it is possible to detect that someone is cogitating such behavior. The resented hate or repressed anger increases the nervous tension and the subject expends much of his cortical power to conceal or inhibit his aggression. Then, when he performs our M.P.D. (myokinetic psychodiagnostic test—see Appendix), the right horizontal line shifts inward, and the right sagittal line forward. Sometimes there is also a downward shift of the right vertical line; this indicates that the subject is worried, introverted, angry, and depressed at the same time. Whenever such deviations increase beyond the individual's limits of resistance, delusions of persecution may appear.

If conditions become worse and the individual continues to be submerged, a schizophrenic reaction may begin, which may be recognized from the axial deviation of the horizontal and sagittal lines and by the typical schizophrenic reversion in the zigzag test of the M.P.D.

Whenever the M.P.D. is impracticable, one may gain insight into the patient's condition by having him perform the Paul Schilder test. He is asked to raise both arms to the horizontal and to keep them extended there with his eyes closed. The observer notes whether the arm deviates slightly outward, the normal reaction, or inward. The latter is due to excess nervous tension, which makes the tone of the adductors more prominent.

Resentful people not only suffer an unbearable existence, but also may become dangerous for the group among which they live and for the cause they are defending. Therefore the psychiatrist must watch them very carefully and must treat all such patients even though they possess high military rank. Otherwise, he will be responsible for military reverses perhaps later explained in terms of overwhelming superiority of the enemy or the like.

SELF-INFLICTED INJURIES

According to the Spanish military code, any soldier who attempted desertion, even by inflicting injury upon himself, was subject to the death penalty unless it could be proved that he did so because of temporary insanity.

When inducting certain members of the fifth column we had to face this problem, and we did so with a psychotherapeutic criterion. Common sense pointed out that when men shoot themselves under such circumstances, they should not be judged and punished in the same way as if they were escaping into the enemy's territory or conveying information to the foe. We therefore claimed the right to prolonged psychiatric observation of such men and soon discovered that among them were many who could be readjusted, later to become excellent fighters. Those men who pleaded guilty and awaited punishment, which was suspended because of the generosity of the military authorities, generally felt obligated to repay this mercy when a proper psychotherapeutic approach made them understand why they had so misbehaved.

Of course, it would be foolish not to watch and control such men carefully over a long period of time. I proposed that they be made half-patients and half-orderlies in the military clinic until their morale was sufficiently restored. I dealt personally with fourteen of these men, eleven of whom became excellent soldiers; one was a real enemy; and the other two developed a schizophrenic reaction.

It is my personal opinion that when one of these cases pleads guilty and confesses that he was planning to avoid the hardships of military service through discharge from the army, he is more likely to recover than when he maintains his false attitude of denial and insists that he hurt himself accidentally. There are, in fact, four different types of case: (1) those who are so afraid of battle that they prefer to face death by suicide; (2) those who attempt to pay for a rest believing that, undetected, they will be brought to the rear to see their relatives or sweethearts; (3) those who want to go over to the enemy but are unable to go through no man's land, and attempt to become detached from the unit to escape; (4) those whose self-mutilation is the first evidence of a mental disorder. The consistent liars belong, of course, in categories (2) and (3); those in group (3) are candidates for concentration camps rather than for any other treatment or attempt at readjustment.

CHAPTER SIX

SPECIFIC DISORDERS

THE PSYCHONEUROTIC REACTIONS

BY PSYCHONEUROSES we understand a morbid aggregate of mental and physical functional disorders which cause the subject intense internal suffering; which are psychologically understandable, although sometimes not purely psychogenic; and which tend to persist and to become aggravated if not properly treated. Neither judgment, reasoning power, nor perceptual functions are affected, but there is a decrease in the objective interests and in the social achievements of the patient. These disorders can be cured only by psychotherapy; physiotherapy may, however, alleviate or even annul some of the symptoms.

As we see, the main features of a psychoneurotic state are: the large amount of subjective suffering, the tendency to chronicity, the maintenance of contact, and the relief afforded by psychotherapy. In conditions of peace, almost all neurotic patients manifest emotional instability and psychopathic trends, with a history of being bright, introverted, precociously worrisome children. They usually exhibit high degrees of cerebrotonia and ectomorphy when somatotyped by the Sheldon-Stevens technique.

THE PSYCHOPATHIC REACTIONS

The psychopathic reactions are to be considered as short periods of psychopathic existence during which the patient almost completely loses his self-control and behaves as if insane. Such outbursts are suddenly released by an external event and even when not properly treated tend toward spontaneous recovery with a tendency to periodic relapses. The patient himself cannot understand why he behaves in this manner. He may explain that he was *"out* of temper" at the moment; scientifically speaking, however, he is never so much *in* his temper as when exhibiting this form of reaction, since it is profoundly rooted in his constitution.

THE ORGANONEUROSES

I agree that the term *organoneuroses* is a misleading one, and yet I retain it as useful for designating certain psychosomatic syndromes in which the symptoms are almost exclusively located in the visceral area of the body image and are objectively referred to a given organ, which thus serves as the turning point of conversion and expression of all the mental conflicts and repressed drives of the individual. This organ is very frequently to be considered, from a physiopathologic point of view, a *locus minoris resistentiae* and so is better able to attract and to focus the attention of the individual. Through it, the somatic and psychic sources of disturbance find a common ground to interlace so intimately that normality can only be restored by the integration of psychic and somatic treatment.

There is no doubt but that in war conditions the psychoneuroses acquire special coloring: they are shortened in evolution and simplified in structure. Whereas in peace we maintain the distinction between hysteria, neurasthenia, compulsive neurosis (psychasthenia), and anxiety neurosis, the core of the overwhelming majority of the war neuroses is constituted by conversion hysteria, to which many other strange mental or physical symptoms may be added. Therefore, instead of concerning himself about the correct designation, the psychiatrist must endeavor to understand the peculiarities of the patient's personality in order to select the most effective method of treatment. This depends less upon the symptom façade than upon the inner aims and ambitions, the cultural equipment, and the psychosomatic constitutional trends. However, in order to fit this work to the use of general practitioners, I shall describe the main forms of psychoneurotic disorders observed at war in accordance with their external manifestations.

PSYCHOMOTOR DISTURBANCES

Tremors.—Tremors are of emotional origin and consist of involuntary, rapid, oscillatory, and rhythmic movements of small amplitude, usually involving the distal parts of the limbs. Muller pointed out that in right-handed persons this type of tremor is always more noticeable on the right side than on the left, and is apparent on the right side alone five times to one.

When these tremors are noted the differential diagnosis rests among disseminated sclerosis, malingering, and chronic alcoholism. The first possibility must be borne in mind because this illness sometimes first appears after an emotional shock. Absent abdominal reflexes, nystagmus, speech difficulties, and other neurological symptoms and laboratory findings will assist the diagnosis in the absence of clinical antecedents. The detection of other signs of chronic alcoholism and the slowness of the tremor, which does not increase when the patient performs intentional movements, help to delimit such cases. As for malingering, it is advisable to (*a*) watch the subject whenever he thinks himself alone and moves about freely; if possible a room with one-way vision should be installed in the clinic; (*b*) have the patient suddenly change the position of his trembling limbs; if there is malingering, a change in rhythm and extent of the tremor is clearly noticeable during and after the execution; and (*c*) observe the patient directly for more than thirty minutes in order to detect the effects of fatigue.

Tics.—Tics are movements that become independent of conscious control, although the subject is somehow aware of them. They almost always have an intelligible motivation: originally purposeful, their automatic repetition beyond the limits of necessity makes them troublesome. In order to merit the designation of tic, the movements must be frequently repeated and compulsive, even though the patient tries to inhibit them.

Of course, tics are more easily simulated than tremors, and therefore one must be very suspicious about people complaining of them. The differential diagnosis from choreic movements must be established, especially if the patient has recently suffered from tonsillitis, rheumatism, or the like. Procedures (*a*) and (*b*), already recommended for detecting false tremors, are also useful here. In addition, we may ask the patient to perform a sequence of movements different from those involved in the tic, and to repeat them regularly: since a genuine tic does not interfere with the patient's will, the ordered movements can easily be accomplished during the tic movements, whereas in cases of malingering the individual is unable to perform both sequences simultaneously, and so attempts to execute them successively.

Spasms and Contractures.—Spasms and contractures of smooth or striated muscles are less frequently observed than the preceding symptoms in war neuroses. Patients suffering from these usually belong to the so-called excitable type, which is related to hypocalcemia. A careful examination must be made in order to eliminate the organic conditions that may be responsible for these symptoms. The existence of a traumatic or inflammatory lesion may be obvious in the case of a wound, or discoverable through inspection, palpation, or radiological methods. Pain and fever are signs that make one suspect an organic, inflammatory factor; the latter must be treated in order to correct the secondary symptoms. In the absence of any other signs, we may conclude that a spasm or contracture is merely functional (hysterical) when it has appeared suddenly, when it corresponds more closely with psychological than with neurological segments of the body, and when its persistence serves the conscious or subconscious purposes of the individual. When the contracture is observed in the limbs, the differentiation of possible articular, muscular, neuritic, and psychological causes is easier than when the spasm is internal, because the former case permits direct examination of the corresponding muscles. One should remember that the most frequent form of organic contracture, associated with radiculitis or funiculitis, affects only the muscles innervated by the corresponding nerve roots.

Pareses and Paralyses.—Weakness or lack of contractility of a single muscle is rarely observed. In war conditions there is a relatively large number of cases of hysterical paresis and paralysis which apparently affect all the muscles—whatever their innervation may be—involved in the execution of socially or professionally purposive movements, thus permitting the individual to avoid actions he is reluctant to perform. In these cases the excitability of the nerves to the paralyzed muscles is conserved, although in some instances reflex responses are altered. Hence an electrical examination suffices to dispel any doubt that may exist.

If the paralysis is unilateral one notes loss of the synkinetic and synergic reflexes, which are retained in cases of organic hemiplegia. On the other hand, the flaccidity of the muscles involved in an hysterical paresis or paralysis is always much less than that observed in the corresponding organic lesions. The differentiation between hysterical and organic paralysis can be established when indirect observation reveals that the paralyzed member recovers its motility when the subject considers himself unobserved. It is worth remembering that hysterical paretic symptoms are twice as frequent on the left side.

Fits.—The epileptic fit is distinguished by typical tonic and clonic phases, complete unconsciousness, absent corneal reflexes, cyanosis, and occasional physical injuries. The latter result from violent muscular contractions and include biting the tongue and dislocation of the elbow or jaw. The seizures are entirely unaffected by an audience and terminate within two or three minutes. Hysterical fits are usually of longer duration, depending upon external environmental factors. The movements are much more irregular and nearly always express rage, erotism, fear, or the like.

The sudden energetic compression of the testis of the male or the mammilla of the female gives rise to a defense reflex and may even stop the hysterical fit, but has no effect on epileptic fits. The best means of making the differential diagnosis, however, is the metrazol (cardiazol, pentamethylenetetrazol) test. The patient, lying on his bed before breakfast, is given an antecubital intravenous injection of the drug, the amount being calculated on the basis of the patient's weight, 0.40 grams for each 65 kilograms. If the fits are of epileptic origin, a grand mal seizure will result within three to five minutes. Before having recourse to this method, it is well to examine the heart and the lungs to exclude organic danger.

Stupor.—Patients in stupor apparently behave in a passive, stupid manner. They exhibit complete lack of initiative, although they may retain some awareness. They may remain motionless for hours, days, or even weeks. It is sometimes possible to make them move by pushing them; at other times, when urgently requested, they fix their gaze upon the examiner. In milder cases they may obey motor commands when the movements are begun by the physician, but when deprived of this help they stop, remaining in abnormal positions. This peculiar state is typical of the *catatonic* syndrome, and in war conditions is frequently observed after air raids, mine explosions, and other dangerous events. It is explicable in terms of inhibition of the cortical area responsible for voluntary movements or of inhibition of the subcortical (midbrain) relay centers which act, so to speak, as a filter, scarcely allowing the passage of the descending cortical impulses. The difference from the state of confusion lies in the fact that whereas in stupor we find a diminution of the *amount* of mental activity, which can even be totally abolished on the motor side, in confusion we find a disorder predominantly in the *perceptual* and in the *intellectual* aspects of the activity, which may or may not affect secondarily the motor reactions of the individual. Consequently, a patient with confusion is always disoriented, but may be aimlessly agitated, whereas a stuporous patient never is agitated, but may be well oriented. Accordingly, stupor is included in the psychomotor and confusion in the purely psychological disturbances.

Agitation.—In a way, we may consider agitation the reverse of stupor, because agitated patients are always restless, react excessively to all stimuli, and exhibit a considerable increase of spontaneous motor initiative. In order to differentiate the possible sources of agitation, one should analyze the motivation, the purpose, the nature, and the results of the actions of the patient. Then one can see whether the agitation is the expression of a state of elation, delirium, or anxiety, or whether it simply evidences a lack of cortical inhibition with increasing excitability of the midbrain centers which give rise to automatic, aimless movements. In the states of elation there is a general overactivity of all the mental functions, but the behavior of the individual is well integrated, and there is a close correspondence among thought content, feeling, and action; the movements are adequate for the purposes, and these are in turn adapted to the desires. The subject is well oriented, and his mood oscillates between joy and rage. In the states of delirium the movements are merely adapted to the content of the dominant delusions: they may be occupational, defensive, or aggressive, but there is always a certain amount of confusion, which establishes diagnosis. As for the states of anxiety, which may or may not be accompanied by disordered intellectual function, the mood of the patients is characteristic and explains their continuous unrest. They oscillate between fear and despair, between indecision and panic, always betraying facial evidence of mental suffering. When the agitation appears deprived of a psychological correlate and the movements are purely automatic, the suspicion of organic disease of the brain arises. A careful neurological examination may detect the existence of a meningitis or meningoencephalitis, either traumatic, toxic, or infectious in origin. In all cases of agitation, lumbar puncture should be performed for therapeutic as well as diagnostic purposes, since in the majority of cases there is increased intracranial pressure.

Elation.—A certain amount of elation is very frequently found among people living under war conditions. The state of elation is the result of the overactivity of all the mental functions, manifesting itself in an increase of amplitude, rapidity, and intensity of the general reactions of the individual. Agitation may be one of the sequelae, and increasing aggressiveness one of the dangers, when the elation becomes too marked. The patient considers himself omniscient and omnipotent; no one can stop him when he thinks he is right, and, unfortunately, he always does; he is interfering and domineering in social relations. Whereas these trends, in mild form, may sometimes be useful, especially in commanders, they are extremely dangerous when exaggerated. All elated individuals must rapidly be isolated and deprived of authority as soon as the M.P.D. (see Appendix) demonstrates their lack of control. These patients can control themselves temporarily and so may appear normal in a rapid, merely verbal examination. The best method of detecting elation is to argue with the suspects, prolonging the conversation on distasteful topics, or to use the above-mentioned test.

Speech Disorders.—Disorders of speech may be the expression of disorders of thought or may originate more specifically in a disturbance of the semantic or the articulatory aspect of the speech function itself. When the speech function is conserved but the individual does not use it, either because of unwillingness or inability, we say that he suffers from *mutism*. When the source of mutism is to be found in the paralysis of the vocal mechanism he is said to have *aphonia:* the individual tries to speak but no sound issues.

Cases of sudden mutism after intense emotions are frequently observed under war conditions; the prognosis is good. Disorders of elocution, in which the individual is intelligible, include *stammering* and *dysarthria.* In the first, the patient is troubled especially by the pronunciation of words that begin with a consonant, and he repeats the first syllable several times until he masters the spasm that prevents him from continuing. In the second, there is failure in the pronunciation of certain letters, especially *r,* and if the patient is given test phrases containing many of these, his speech becomes almost unintelligible. Some special disorders of speech are related to particular diseases of the central nervous system with diagnostic significance, as, for instance, the slow, scanning, colorless, and unemotional speech of multiple sclerosis and the paretic dysarthria of general paresis.

TREATMENT OF PSYCHOMOTOR DISTURBANCES

All the psychomotor disturbances can be considered to be the result of disorder in the different paths of the central nervous system. This disorder may result from a diminution, an increase, or a disintegration of nervous impulses affecting local or general areas. Whatever the cause, the outcome is the loss of functional unity and the impairment of reactive equilibrium. From a practical point of view, the treatment of all the symptoms of psychomotor disorders lies in the restoration of normal conditions by means of proper psychotherapeutic influences which may be supplemented with physical or chemical means. Conflicting inhibitions and excitations may be the cause as well as the effect of almost all these disturbances and may also contribute to the state known as nervous exhaustion. Hence, the first therapeutic measure is to isolate the patient and to afford him the proper amount of rest, food, and security for the spontaneous restoration of his psychic energies. This treatment should not be continued too long, however, because the individual may profit from it by trying to escape his military duties. In order to accelerate readjustment, the external imposition of rhythmic movements is necessary to release inhibitions and to increase excitation to normal. The psychotherapist must convey to the patient his belief in the absolute and rapid success of this treatment. This belief will be increased by the assertions of convalescent patients. The tonic effect of a proper psychotherapeutic atmosphere is far more important than the technique of treatment selected. Let us briefly examine the methods of treating the different disorders.

Tremors.—Execution of complex movements requiring increasing dissociation of the two sides is valuable. These movements must first be performed passively, under the pressure of the psychotherapist, and then followed by increasing voluntary effort on the part of the patient. Finally, the movements must be accomplished against the active resistance of the psychotherapist, who will profit from all the changes in direction, pressure, and speed to show the patient how the tremor may be interrupted or modified. Once this result has been obtained, a new sequence of rhythmic, slow, oscillatory movements is begun under the guidance of the psychotherapist. If the tremor persists, no sign of impatience is shown by the psychiatrist, but the movements are continued with the command: "Go on; keep moving at the same speed. Don't be nervous; everything is all right; you are improving. You will be cured today, even if it is necessary to remain here for hours. Try to obtain a good rhythm; breathe slowly and in time with your movements: one, two, one, two. That is perfect . . ." and so on. The important thing is to inspire in the patient the belief that he is dominated by the overwhelming personal power of his opponent. It is amazing how easily these functional disorders disappear as soon as this belief is obtained.

Tics, Spasms, and Choreic Movements.—If the diagnosis of the psychogenic nature of these has been established, we may use either hypnotic treatment or direct suggestion combined with (*a*) exercises of muscular relaxation and (*b*) exercises of passive, active, and opposed motion of the affected member under the control of the therapist. These exercises must be continued rhythmically until the symptom is controlled. No complaint on the part of the patient is admissible; he must feel that the only deliverance from the exercises is the disappearance of the disorder.

Pareses and Paralyses.—Under no circumstances must the patient be permitted to lie in bed. He must be obliged to stand up and to move, either actively or passively, the paretic or paralyzed members every five or ten minutes. Occasionally, if he complains of fatigue or refuses to co-operate, a painful faradic current is applied to the region —under the pretense that it serves to increase the strength of the nerves—and the exercises are continued, always in rhythm with respiration. Sometimes, as in the cases of hysterical paraplegia, the physician will be obliged to place himself behind the patient and hold him by the arms, pushing the patient's legs with his knees as if he were a puppet. As soon as a slight improvement is noted, the rate and amplitude of the movement should be increased.

Fits.—Most important is to make a precise diagnosis. If the fits are of an hysterical character the best treatment is to ignore them or to stop them by violent pressure upon algetic points. Compression of the testis or mammilla serves as well for treatment as for diagnosis. If the fits are of an epileptic nature the patient must be relieved of duties that require steady attention or responsibility and should then be given the ordinary treatment for epilepsy. Whatever the nature of the convulsions, it is always wise to perform a lumbar puncture, and if the intracranial pressure is increased or decreased, to restore normality by the proper measures of hypertonic or hypotonic solutions (Wood's technique).

Stupor.—Intravenous injections of sodium amytal, repeated daily, or electroconvulsions are the best available methods of treatment.

Agitation.—If there is a psychological cause of the agitation, psychotherapy is indicated; if no cause can be ascertained, the best treatment is "permanent subnarcosis," applicable in cases of anxiety as well. The technique is described elsewhere in this book.

Elation.—Isolation; rhythmic, monotonous, and tiresome physical labor; prolonged tepid baths; the usual sedatives—these constitute the treatment of elation.

Speech Disorders.—"It is not necessary to speak in order to fight" —this slogan has been frequently repeated by commanders in the army, but the difficulty is that: "It is necessary to speak in order to command," and speech disorders are especially frequent among those who are entrusted with this task. There are many different ways of dealing with speech disorders (Stinchfield). We shall consider only those that are most effective in war conditions.

Hysterical Mutism or Aphonia.—The best method is to submit the subject to the action of a prolonged and intermittent aspiration of ether, as if to obtain general anesthesia, terminating administration of ether when the subject begins to sleep, i. e., immediately after the second (excitatory) phase is passed. Profiting from the supposed unconsciousness of the patient, the physician comments on the case to his assistants: "He will be all right, but may require two or three hours' work." Each time the patient looks at the physician, the latter must touch his neck with his hand and say: "Try to pronounce a-a-ah. Come on; you will feel that the control of your voice is increasing continuously because with the anesthesia we are removing the obstacle that prevented you from commanding it."

We have not failed in a single case with this method. Usually the result is obtained after four or five trials; sometimes many more will be required, but the essential is that the subject be convinced that he will remain on the operating table until his speech returns.

In the other disorders, the best treatment is to transfer the individual to new duties in which there is the same or more personal danger, but for which the correct pronunciation of words is not necessary.

SENSORY AND PERCEPTUAL NEUROTIC DISORDERS

Hysterical Blindness.—Whenever possible, the patient complaining of blindness should be examined by an ophthalmologist in order to avoid confusion between the central and the organic forms of the disorder. If ophthalmologic consultation is impossible at the moment, we may reach a correct diagnosis by performing the following tests:

a) Ask the patient to relax his eyelids as much as possible; then the examiner suddenly tries to open them with his fingers. In hysterical blindness the patient exhibits an active and increasing resistance to such a maneuver and, when forced to keep his eyes open, almost always turns them up to avoid the glance of the examiner.

b) If we succeed in surprising the patient with a flash of light, the pupillary reflex is obtained.

c) Demand that the patient walk about a room submitted to sudden changes of intensity of illumination, asking him to perform

a simple mental task at the same time, such as adding serial numbers
in a loud voice. Whenever his attention is directed to the mental
work, his gait is altered by the changes of light intensity, and vice
versa.

d) When instructed to proceed in an open space, in which some
apparent obstacles have been strategically located, the hysteric goes
more slowly and turns more than the really blind.

e) Asked to light a match, the hysterically blind patient hesitates
and exhibits emotional tremor in attempting to give the impression of
ineptitude.

We may suspect either hysterical blindness or plain malingering
whenever the behavior of the patient is altered by the presence of
spectators or by the examination. If doubt persists, the best we can
do is treat the case as if it were hysteria, since the psychotherapeutic
approach will do no harm in the event of organic blindness. The
easiest treatment is to keep the patient in complete darkness, in-
forming him that the next day a test will be made, according to the
results of which a delicate operation may be considered. A nurse
will later explain to the patient that if the retina retains any sensibility he should be able at least to distinguish light from darkness
when brought into a somewhat brighter room. Of course, deprivation
of light carries with it isolation, so that loneliness augments the
desire to recover. The next day, with the aid of a simple suggestive
device, such as the injection of distilled water, the patient is given
the opportunity to regain his vision under the verbal and personal
pressure of the psychotherapist.

Deafness.—Hysterical deafness, if not associated with mutism,
is easily treated by transferring the subject to the noisiest place
available—the artillery service in the army zone, the auction room in
the rear—announcing that this is the suitable work for him until
he recovers his hearing.

Anesthesia.—Anesthesia is usually accompanied by paretic or
spastic phenomena which must be treated first. A simple way of

dealing with the anesthesia itself is to neglect it, or, if the patient claims that his anesthesia prevents the performance of his duties, to apply strong faradic currents. A prior neurological examination should, of course, be performed to avoid mistakes. Hysterical anesthesia shows an irregular, bizarre distribution over the skin; it is total; and it involves deep sensibility, since the patient claims that he cannot feel pressure either. In spite of this, the patient sometimes complains of sudden severe pains in the region. When one deals with clever patients, the local injection of a real anesthetic solution (novocaine or solucaine, etc.) helps to confuse them and obviates the need for consultations.

Pains.—Hysterical or psychogenic pains are a source of trouble whenever a real injury has been previously suffered by the patient. There is no use in attempting a classification of these pains. The diagnosis, whatever the location, is based upon (*a*) the absence of organic signs of physical pain (midriasis, pulse changes on pressure, facial pallor, etc.); (*b*) lack of correspondence between the extent of the painful area and the defense reflexes of the underlying muscular planes; (*c*) exaggeration of subjective complaints when the patient is observed or attended; and (*d*) lack of relation between the complaints and the action of real analgesic substances administered to the patient without letting him know what they are. The best way to handle hysterical pains in the psychiatric centers of the front line in the Spanish War was to begin gymnastic exercises immediately with the help of the psychiatrist, making use of verbal and motor compulsion, words, and actions.

Introceptive Reflex and Visceral Symptoms.—Visceral symptoms are the core of the organoneurotic states which in the present war seem to be the substitute invented by the—let us call it subconscious—minds of the war neurotics. As Dr. Gillespie said in his Salmon lectures, there are fashions in medicine. We must admit that the average man already knows too much about the rough and ready way in which the explicit forms of conversion hysteria were handled in the last war, so that this time the patients themselves are creating a new path for their neurotic derangements by means of a process of interiorization of the symptoms.

Symptoms most commonly observed are: disorders of swallowing, gastric spasms, vomiting, diarrhea, aerophagy, false obstruction of the bowels, paroxysmal tachycardia, stenocardia, etc. The first measure to adopt in dealing with such cases is to call into consultation the corresponding specialists in internal medicine. The second is to establish a "dynamic and pluralistic psycho-somato-social approach," as Dr. Adolph Meyer calls it. The patients must continue some work for the benefit of their units even though they remain in bed for observation.

A third rule is the avoidance of intense chemical treatment, with the alternative recourse to abundant physiotherapy, verbal suggestion, and persuasion. Simultaneously the truly psychotherapeutic—human and cheerful—contact between the psychiatrist and the patient must be established. The latter must be relieved of his feelings of worry and disgust; insight must be obtained into what is disturbing him: perhaps he is depressed because he lacks news from home, or has feelings of guilt because he failed to help a companion in a tragic situation, or is concealing a hatred against someone. In brief, because of the more complicated structure of the psychosomatic syndromes, psychiatrists cannot handle them with the simple and ingenuous assumption that all they need is emphatic assertions of quick recovery, as do the average cases of fright neurosis.

The organoneurotic cases tend to become more and more introverted, demand sedatives or operations, and object to being treated in the psychiatric clinics since they do not regard themselves as mentally ill. Their syndromes oscillate between the neurasthenic and hypochondriacal states on the one hand, and the real somatoses (somatic illnesses, produced by infectious, toxic, or degenerative processes) on the other. This is why such patients create confusion wherever they are placed.

GENERAL RULES FOR PSYCHOSOMATIC TREATMENT

In addition to what has already been said, I feel compelled to emphasize some general points that must be kept in mind by military physicians, especially psychiatrists, in dealing with war neurotics.

a) Take care to locate the patient in the most suitable companionship according to his personality trends. This means selection of bed neighbors.

b) Avoid clinotherapy as much as chemotherapy.

c) Begin the medical examination at the somatic level. Simultaneously observe and analyze the expressions—gestural, attitudinal, lexical, and pantomimic; later attempt to gain insight into the cultural and intellectual background. Finally reach the intimate, affective realm and inquire as to beliefs, interests, vices, drives, etc.

d) Always speak to the patient in the absence of other patients and lay people. Do not question him about what is not really necessary for the diagnostic procedure.

e) Keep all the subjective complaints well separated from the objective findings for purposes of comparison. Do not mix either with your inferences.

f) Remember that a wise remark may have a beneficial effect even in cases of organic illness. Also bear in mind that whatever therapy you choose, it will have a psychological influence for either good or bad: which of the two, depends upon the faith you create or the fear you arouse in the patient.

g) Fight against passivity as much as against excitement. Try to create a good living program for the patients and assure them a suitable distribution of work, enjoyment, and rest. Organize in a well-planned manner the social group on the ward.

TRAUMATIC NEUROSES

Two American contributions to the subject of the traumatic neuroses have recently made their appearance. Both have come from the psychoanalytic school. I refer to Abram Kardiner's *The Traumatic Neuroses of War,* and the excellent article of Sandor Rado, "The Traumatic Neuroses." Although my point of view coincides with theirs to a large extent, I wish to point out some differences and to cite my personal experiences. To begin, the term "traumatic neuroses" should be limited to the neurotic disturbances unchained but not directly determined by a physical (cranial) trauma. In so far as the psychic behavior of a man who has been buried or blown over by a shell expresses the somatic consequences of the mechanical insult, we should refrain from placing him in this group of cases. We must do so, however, as soon as we detect that the mental symptoms are the mere consequences of a subconscious arrangement which the post-traumatic situation has made possible.

The patient's comrades have rushed upon him, asked how he felt, whether he was injured and what they could do for him; or perhaps he lost consciousness and was brought to a campaign hospital, thus encouraging him to believe that he was really ill. In this manner the most favorable circumstances are created to allow the man to resolve the conflict between his sense of duty and his desire for protection and self-preservation. In the measure that the patient considers himself a war casualty and behaves accordingly, he not only deserves attention, affection, and praise from the outside world, but also feels satisfaction and gratification within himself.

The psychosomatic approach is, of course, the only one that permits complete understanding of the intricacy of the two groups of symptoms—those expressing on the psychological level the disturbances of the soma and those expressing on the somatic plane the conflicts within the mind. This is the reason why psychiatrists must be very careful not to deal with such cases in a rough and ready manner. My pupil, Tosquelles, working at the Extremadura front, found a lowering of the convulsive threshold as determined by metrazol injections in all his cases of traumatic neuroses. His findings lend weight to the above advice.

The symptoms of traumatic neuroses may be localized about the injured part of the body and appear purely somatic or—and this is of more concern to our present discussion—may be limited to the psychological or conscious spheres.

TRAUMATIC AMNESIA

Inability to recall experiences either immediately before or after the traumatic incident, or the events directly related to the shock itself, is a common event in war. "Paradoxical inhibition" is responsible for this failure. In any case of amnesia we must determine whether (*a*) there is an impairment in the apprehension of new stimuli, (*b*) the patient can identify the forgotten memories when someone presents them to him verbally in order to refresh his memory, and (*c*) there are other mental disorders, such as Ganser's syndrome, pseudodementia, stupor, etc.

The impairment in the apprehension of incoming stimuli gives rise to the amnestic complex. Whenever present, it points to the existence of an encephalopathic (i. e., organic) disorder.

The inability to acknowledge the traumatic experience may result either from psychogenic repression, in which the patient tries to avoid the renewal of unpleasant feelings, or to a lack of comprehension, in which the patient is unable to understand the logical meaning of the associative bonds that convert the presented material into a meaningful psychological content.

Whenever a psychogenic repression is the cause of the amnesia the so-called cathartic methods of pressing interrogation under suggestion or mild hypnosis must be used. If the postcommotional amnesia is due to transient encephalopathic phenomena (diaschisis theory of Monakow) the patient is drowsy and confused and does not exhibit an impairment of memory so much as a general collapse of the intellectual activities. Proper treatment for such a state is lumbar puncture, quiet, vitamins, and means to restore the normal blood pressure.

There is also the possibility that the traumatic amnesia may be secondary to epileptic fits, developed during the traumatic incident. In order to make a correct diagnosis, the hypoalgesia of the skin area limited by the mid-line and the fifth and sixth cervical segments in both arms must be sought (according to Muskens).

APROSEXIA

Weakness of concentration and of the power of abstraction is a frequent complaint especially of commanding officers, when subjected to a traumatic incident after a period of overstrain. This is one of the main symptoms of the neurasthenic syndrome, but can also appear alone. The M.P.D. furnishes a good basis for the differentiation of the underlying nervous and mental causes (see Appendix). The first procedure is the search for a sinus infection, tuberculosis, or diabetes; in the absence of other disorders, phosphorous preparations, relief from duty, and careful subsequent retraining are advisable. Benzedrine may also be used if there is low blood pressure.

FUGUES

Soldiers who run away from their military duties after a trauma and are apprehended by their own comrades frequently say that they cannot remember what happened, or else admit that they were seized by an overwhelming impulse to escape forward. Psychiatrists are then called upon to decide whether such individuals should or should not be considered deserters, and whether they deserve to be punished or treated. In order to assist the diagnostic procedure, I advance the following scheme of fugue motivation. A fugue, occurring either immediately after a traumatic incident or somewhat later, may be:

NATURE	MOTIVE	TYPE
(a) Psychogenic	A mental conflict	Psychopathic reaction (a)
	A false belief	Paranoid delusion (b)
	Uncontrolled realization of a wish	Dreamed: hysterical somnambulism (c)
		Impulsive and uncritical: feeble-minded (d)
(b) Psychopathologic (mixed or psychosomatic etiology)	Symbolic protest, defense, or ceremonial against "magic" powers	Compulsive (e)
	Negativistic tendency No direct purpose but still able to exhibit a situational insight	Schizophrenic reactions (f)
(c) Organic or encephalopathic	Lack of planning and adaptation. The subject is delirious, confused, or in a twilight state, sometimes unable to speak. He behaves as an automaton	Traumatic delirium (g)
		Alcoholic delirium (tremens) (h)
		Epileptic (twilight) dromomanic state (i)
		Infectious and toxic psychoses (including general paresis) (j)

Of course, an alternative to be considered is that the fugue has been willfully and deliberately planned by the subject who wants to profit from being temporarily confused (k). Only a careful psychological and psychiatric consultation can give insight as to the type (a–k) of the fugue. Here again the M.P.D. may prove useful for the detection of malingering.

PHOBIC STATES

After a traumatic incident an increased fear of danger is frequently observed. Whenever this fear exceeds the limits of reasonable expectation we may speak of traumatophobia. Through the irradiation of the negative conditioned reflex created by the previous injury, the individual feels afraid as soon as he perceives any sensory stimulus associated with the traumatic one. Two special groups of stimuli thus become frightening: the sound of noises and the sight of moving spots in the sky. The first is connected with shell explosions, the second with airplanes. Dozens of wounded soldiers, at the beginning of the Spanish War, rose from their beds and rushed toward the staircase of the ward as soon as they heard the air-raid signal (noise phobia). Many of them were also frightened by the humming of the motors of the incoming ambulances. The airplane phobia was so intense among some convalescents that they were continually examining the sky and were even upset by the sight of harmless sparrows. Whenever these phobias are observed there is lack of inhibitory power, and restoration must consist of progressive, experimental reconditioning, in association with sedatives and special respiratory exercises. As a matter of fact, almost all these patients are of the "hyperthymic" or "emotive" temperament, are predisposed to anxiety, fond of intellectual and imaginative activities, and reluctant to indulge in sports. The best treatment is to alter their habits of life and to displace their mental energies from the contemplative to the reactive field. They must be trained to engage in gymnastic and athletic exercises, to perform complicated movements requiring all their mental powers, while submitted to the disturbing presence of the phobogenic stimuli. As soon as possible they should be transferred to the center of recuperation and retraining, where the psychological environment is far more stimulating than that of the psychiatric unit. Mild hypnosis is sometimes useful to accelerate the cure, but this must always be supplemented by the progressive contact of the patient with the danger signals in the presence of the psychotherapist.

INFECTIOUS AND TOXIC PSYCHOSES

The infectious and toxic psychoses, the so-called exogenous forms of reaction, are increased in war conditions. Rheumatic, intestinal, and respiratory infections, which in peacetime conditions would elapse without determining abnormal psychological reactions, are now frequently accompanied by mental disorders. The same is true for the states of acute chemical intoxication from the ingestion of spoiled food. The threshold of delusional and hallucinatory reactions is lowered because of the relative exhaustion of the higher nervous centers. Through lack of sleep the patients become more prone to plunge into dreamlike states. They are neither awake nor asleep, and so the boundaries between the external, real, world and the internal, fantastic, world almost vanish. Then the noxious action of the virus or chemical toxin upon the higher nervous centers is magnified by the lack of resistance, and all possible varieties of twilight delusions and pseudoperceptions occur.

These cases require the combination of antitoxic and restorative treatments. The use of strong sedatives and opium preparations should be strictly forbidden, but should be replaced by injections of liver extract, vitamins B and C, hypertonic solutions, and the practice of a fixation abscess whenever the patient is much agitated. In fact, I have obtained the best results from the injection of 1 c.c. of old turpentine solution (spirits of oil of turpentine) in the lumbar region about two or three centimeters deep. The advantages of the subsequent local inflammation are noticeable not only in the psychic sphere, but in the improvement of the general somatic state as well. The sole contraindication to such a procedure is the existence of severe acute nephritis. There is no objection, when the patient is heavy and the agitation very intense, to repeating the injection on the other side of the lumbar region if the sedative effects of the first have not appeared within twenty-four hours.

A warning must be issued against the tendency to transfer these patients from psychiatric to medical wards and vice versa, according to the predominance of mental or physical symptoms. These changes are always pernicious for the patient, since they involve a loss of time and increase the patient's confusion. The average psychiatrist as well as the average physician can and must deal with these cases; if special doubt exists, it is always better to call for the advice of the corresponding specialist than to move the patient from his bed to transfer him to another hospital.

SYMPTOMATIC PSYCHOSES

In war conditions the most common symptomatic psychoses are (*a*) the association of a diabetic state with symptoms of depression and anxiety; (*b*) the association of paranoid and catatonic schizophrenic reactions with the reactivation of old pulmonary tuberculosis; and (*c*) the "hypertensive" psychoses (Krapf). Closely connected with these cases, although of quite different nature, are some of the cases of neurocirculatory asthenia or cardiovascular neurosis accompanied by mental symptoms. Whereas in the latter cases, according to W. H. Dunn, we are dealing with psychosomatic disorders, in the group to which we are now referring we are dealing with somatopsychic disturbances. In the DaCosta syndrome the complaints are somatic but the treatment must be psychological; in the cases of symptomatic psychoses, the apparent disorders are mental but the fundamental therapy must be somatic.

Accordingly, I favor the use of the first phase of the Sakel treatment (ten units of insulin injected every six hours, fifteen minutes before meals) whenever a psychotic or even psychopathic patient evidences a tendency toward a diabetic curve in the glucose-tolerance test. I advise high doses of vitamins A and D and calcium injections for patients complaining of depressions or delusions and showing signs of tuberculosis. Whenever high blood pressure is detected in a mental patient, especially if he is old, the treatment of this symptom should be considered the most important procedure regardless of the mental picture.

Therefore, practical advice for dealing with the mental casualties of war is routinely to perform a glucose-tolerance test or at least to examine the urine for sugar, to obtain an X-ray of the chest, and to determine the blood pressure. In my Psychiatric Clinic of the Third Military Region I had not less than 6 per cent positive findings that showed this somatopsychic type of reaction, and I believe that we must not forget it at present when psychosomatic interpretations have become so fashionable.

DIFFERENTIAL DIAGNOSIS OF THE DEPRESSIVE STATES

Since depression is so common among military men after a long period of war, I think that it deserves special diagnostic attention. No adequate treatment can be advised, nor a valid prognosis made, until something is known of the cause for the depression in any particular case. Therefore the description of the following forms is more than of purely academic value.

1. *Physiogenic or Symptomatic Depression.*—This form belongs to the symptomatic psychoses previously mentioned and is the most frequent of that group. The patient feels tired and inefficient, complains that even the simplest acts are exhausting, and attempts to avoid any muscular exertion. Intellectual work also becomes difficult, making him feel empty-headed or heavy-headed; special pains, preferentially located in the neck, annoy him; his thoughts seem to vanish and he feels insecure. This picture is very close to the neurasthenic syndrome, but may be differentiated from it because the personal reaction toward the symptoms is normal: the patient tries to accomplish his tasks and in spite of the lowering of his biotone enjoys relaxation in good company. We might say that in this form the consciousness is aware of the disturbance within the organism, but can avoid total personal suffering. The M.P.D. shows depression (downward shift) in the verticals, especially the right, and slight insecurity in the zigzag lines, but the complex shapes are maintained; aggression and introversion remain within normal limits.

2. *Affective (Simple) Depression.*—Vital activity is maintained but its autoperception is distorted and decreased. The thymopsyche, or zone of the mind that integrates somatic and visceral sensations into a feeling tone of well-being or the opposite, is affected. The patients

feel strong and mentally normal, but complain that they have lost almost completely the *joie de vivre* and that they are unable to experience anything but annoyance and weariness. When asked to perform an action, they inquire: "What for?" On the other hand, the emotional impact of ordinary stimuli upon them is also blunted. The striking paradox that describes these patients is that *what they feel most is that they do not feel,* because the memories of previous emotions are more vivid and bright than their experiences in the present.

Kurt Schneider speaks of *vital depression* in regard to these cases, but I should prefer the term *affective depression,* since the rest of the mentality remains normal. Treatment involves the use of electric shocks, benzedrine, alcoholic beverages, etc., according to the circumstances. Psychotherapy is useful only if it succeeds in convincing the patient to perform his duties even though he does not believe in them and has lost his faith in the values and goals of living. Our M.P.D. shows more introversion (shifting inward of the horizontals) than depression (shifting downward of the verticals) in these cases.

3. *Melancholy Depression.*—For this form the proper name would be *dysthymia,* or, perhaps, *compression* instead of *depression.* In fact, the technique of our M.P.D. confirms the view of those of the Freudian school who assert that melancholy patients are not merely sad but furious against themselves. Such patients present feelings of guilt and of need for autopunition, which sometimes lead them to self-destruction. All the individual's energies are stored against the ego; the patient blames himself and considers himself a negative element, if not a monster. Autoaggression is shown in this form by the shift of the sagittal lines, but there is also a great deal of introversion (shifting inward of the horizontals) and sometimes a certain amount of anxiety (continuous increase of size and acceleration of the movements). This kind of psychosis belongs to the group of the manic-depressive (endogenous) disturbances. Its treatment must not be undertaken in military clinics, and it is a cause of honorable discharge in war conditions.

4. *Agitated (Anxious) Depression.*—This form, admitted only by British and American psychiatrists, differs from the preceding in that the patient does not feel depressed, but is rather in a state of hyperphrenia with disorientation and irresolution. Whereas in melancholia the underlying emotion was rage against the ego, in this form the underlying emotion is a blending of rage and fear. The patient feels disturbed, expecting a great disaster, although he cannot say how or why such a terrible event will happen. Frequently he misinterprets events and develops feelings of persecution (spy-phobia); somatic functions are severely impaired (sitophobia and sleeplessness are almost constant). This form is shown by the M.P.D. to be more closely connected with schizophrenia than with the manic-depressive constellation. The emergency treatment on the field may consist either of permanent subnarcosis or of the turpentine abscess. Hypoglycemic shock and subconvulsive electric shocks are better than full-dose insulin or electric convulsions.

If the M.P.D. shows the signs of an underlying schizophrenic process (schizophrenic reversions—see Appendix) the patient must be discharged from military service. If not, he may be treated in the military clinic of the rear zone. Psychotherapy is almost useless in this form.

5. *Psychogenic or Reactive Depression.*—Psychogenic or reactive depressions are characterized by the existence of a concrete situation which explains, although it does not entirely justify, the psychic behavior. The patient has been struck by a great disaster or disappointment and is unable to go on with his life and repress or forget the unpleasant things connected with the situation. His ego is submerged in the constant reconsideration and recall of the painful events, and he cannot make up his mind to direct the stream of consciousness toward the future. The more he broods, the farther he is from a state of inner composure; but this does not negate the beneficial effects of a good psychotherapeutic approach. All that these patients need is the mental relief of an understanding friend who restates the situation troubling them and opens new paths of

action. As soon as the circumstances appear favorable to offer a solution for discharging the grief or remorse by suggesting another business undertaking, a change of living habits, a change of environment, a transference of affections, a refuge in religious faith, etc., the patient recovers his normal health without any other medical help.

These psychogenic depressions reveal themselves in the M.P.D. by a downward shift of the leading hand in the vertical plane, whereas the uneducated hand maintains the level; there is also a pronounced inward shift of the horizontal movements of the leading hand (see Appendix).

6. *Conative Depression* (*Apathy or Abulia*).—Lack of initiative and enthusiasm is frequent among drafted men who do not realize the ethical basis of the task they are called upon to perform. Of course, this is not truly a question of depression but rather of indifference and disinterest.

The term "conative depression" must be reserved for the mental attitude of frustrated individuals who are called by the French psychiatrists *ratés* or *détraqués*. The social factor plays an important part in these cases: the patients are convinced a posteriori that they will never realize success in life. They feel that they are mere pawns and so renounce the direction and planning of their lives. A patient who is conatively depressed merely exists; he does not live. He has lost his self-esteem and dignity and has become completely indifferent. He is resigned to descend step by step, becoming a gambler, a sexual pervert, or a delinquent. Neither the inferiority complex nor the admission of an asthenic, constitutional factor or a schizoid temperament exhausts the motivation of this form, so frequently observed among people coming from the outskirts of great metropolitan areas.

Such subjects must almost always be treated in an artificial environment, which provides easier possibilities for the achievement of initial triumphs. When they hear praise from the outside they begin to recover their self-esteem. The proper selection of a small group of companions to create a psychotherapeutic atmosphere about the patient is the best method for assisting the psychiatrist, who in these cases plays the role of an educator.

7. *Schizophrenic Depression.*—Last but not least we come to the description of this clinical form which is rather a withdrawal than a depression. The patients suffering from this syndrome are under the influence of an increasing *internal* inhibition which may even lead to catatonic stupor. We must not be misled by their external appearance, however, since at any moment they may commit explosive, aggressive acts of unusual violence.

The differential diagnosis between a schizophrenic and a manic-depressive depression is easily established by the M.P.D. Patients affected by the schizophrenic form allow their hands to shift down in the verticals, but, most important, exhibit such predominance of the flexor attitude that the zigzag test shows the characteristic schizophrenic reversal (see plates in Appendix). In addition, there is bending in the sagittal movements with a tendency to lose the sharpness, clearness, and regularity of the complex forms, such as the chains, throughout the M.P.D. Of course, in advanced cases, the analysis of the verbal content allows for easy diagnosis, but sometimes that cannot be performed because of mutism.

In order to overcome the initial stupor, which may prevent the performance of the M.P.D., an intravenous injection of 4 or 5 c.c. of sodium amytal may be given one or two hours before the test. Proper subsequent treatment includes the combination of metrazol or electric-shock therapy with liver extract, vitamins, occupational therapy, and medical gymnastics.

Of course, I agree that an attempt like the above to classify depressions cannot provide for all the possible variations of individual cases. Sometimes a given patient shows a combination of two or more of the syndromes described above, and therefore our psychiatric work becomes so difficult. The obstacles to good insight into each case may be considerably reduced, however, when the physician bears in mind the standard types of the depressive syndrome and so avoids fundamental errors in diagnosis and treatment.

CHAPTER SEVEN

RECOVERY AND READJUSTMENT

READJUSTMENT AND REALLOCATION OF RECOVERED MENTAL CASUALTIES

A GENERAL principle to be kept in mind by military psychiatrists is that though they may be tolerant and even generous when inducting men into the army, rejecting for combat services even the doubtful cases, *once a man has been enrolled and trained as a soldier all efforts should be made to keep him in the army* in the event that he becomes ill or injured. In other words, even if there are sufficient new recruits, *it is always preferable to restore a veteran rather than to replace him by a novice.*

Some of the reasons for such a principle are (*a*) the saving of time and energy required in the training period; (*b*) the decrease in future applicants for life pensions (France was obliged to create an entire ministry for this); (*c*) the prevention of depressive feelings which arise when the subject considers himself useless; (*d*) the avoidance of the demoralizing influences that such cases, returned to civil life, usually have upon their social environment.

A second principle to observe is to attempt to send the recovered soldier back to the same unit whence he came and where his friends are. A new adjustment to a quite different unit may lead the individual to give information and to make comparisons and comments that are more harmful than beneficial.

A third principle is, once the man has been cured, to attempt to go back over the cause and to profit from this experience to prevent relapse. This means that sometimes a change must be made of his assignment within the unit to which he belongs; at other times, it is not the assignment but the immediate social surroundings that must be changed; and at still other times, it is neither the assignment nor the surroundings but the attitude of his superiors toward him.

Finally, many cases of mental liabilities proved to be determined by lack of military information or training, and also by a technical defect in the performance of military duties, such as, for instance, a tendency to isolation during the battle, lack of camouflage, insufficient orientation, etc.

The possibility exists of such heavy losses of men in the unit that it becomes inadvisable to send the few survivors back, since they will always remember their old "pals" and resent the newcomers. Therefore, transferal from the psychiatric ward to the front line should be made through the mediation of another service, which can test the actual fitness of the combatant, help him to recondition himself, and also correct possible defects of military technique. Such centers should be located, if possible, just behind the front line—so that military discipline will be at its height—but may be administered under the advice of the psychiatrist in each particular case.

RECOVERY AND RETRAINING CENTERS IN THE SPANISH REPUBLICAN ARMY

Men leaving our psychiatric military clinics were transferred to recovery and retraining centers. Here the patient was asked his opinion about (*a*) the causes and motivations of his own disorder; (*b*) his insight into his own physical and mental capacities; (*c*) whether or not he wished to return to the same military activity, and, if not, why. Once the personal opinions, desires, and plans of the recovered individual had been obtained, the classification officer and the physician were called to decide whether he was ready for active military service. Whenever possible, the special advice of the military psychiatric clinic that had treated him was observed. Of course, however, the reallocation of such men had to be carried out in accordance with the military requirements of the moment. As soon as his immediate future was decided, the man was submitted to the corresponding special training, and his teachers were called upon to deliver, twice weekly, a report on his progress.

Particular attention was devoted in such centers to developing games and competitive sports in the hours of recreation. To observe the behavior of the men enjoying a football game or a motion picture revealed more about their mental state than the procedure of watching them during the performance of their duties. Accordingly, ample occasions for entertainment were supplied. Twice weekly a call for volunteers was made; these volunteers were to take charge of various special assignments in the center. This allowed the observers to establish a less formal contact with the men and to obtain far better insight into the morale of the group. The maximum time allowed for the stay in such recovery centers was four weeks.

Special military maneuvers and tactical exercises for reconditioning were organized in the centers. Special emphasis was placed upon those physical exercises requiring teamwork and co-operation, such as medicine ball, relay races, etc. In addition, frequent discussions concerning problems of morale were held under the supervision of the morale officers or the visiting psychiatrist.

RELATIVE INCIDENCE AND RECOVERY RATE OF MENTAL CASUALTIES IN THE ARMY AND CIVILIAN POPULATION DURING THE RECENT SPANISH WAR

To evaluate the work outlined, reference must be made to the absolute and relative incidence of mental casualties in the Spanish Republican Army as compared with that among civilians, and to the percentage of recovered and readjusted cases. To begin, we may quote the data supplied by Professor Dr. José Puche, General Inspector of Military Medicine, concerning the total casualties in two different regions of the army zone. The Madrid front was stable during 1938; it was the site of a war of positions. In the Ebro front, on the other hand, there was a war of movement. On the Madrid front we suffered six hundred thousand casualties in that year, analyzable as follows:

52.36% wounded
40.35% sick
1.05% undiagnosed
6.24% killed

From the sick cases, we had 12.63 per cent infectious and parasitic diseases and *only 0.432 per cent mental cases!*

In the Ebro front during three months of fierce battle 120,000 casualties were registered, classified as follows:

68.4% wounded
24.1% killed
7.5% sick

Among this percentage of sick the mental group constituted *only 0.25 per cent of the total!*

The recovered cases among the wounded who were transferred to the surgical wards of the campaign hospitals were in all 88 per cent; 6 per cent were discharged from the army and the remaining 6 per cent died.

As for the mental casualties, I can offer the last report of my Military Clinic of the Third Region, delivered in December, 1938, when the war was practically over and our morale was reaching its lowest ebb.

Summary of the Activities of the Psychiatric Clinic of Vilaboi (Third Military Region) during December, 1938:

Occupied beds on the first of December 114
Admissions during December 122
Discharges during December 126
Occupied beds on the first of January 110

The 126 discharges were distributed as follows:

Recovered: Reincorporated in the unit 46

Sent to the Special Neuropsychiatric Tribunal and
judge by it as totally fit 3

fit for auxiliary services 38

Sent to the Naval Tribunal 4

Sent to the International Sanitary Tribunal (I.B.) ... 2

Not Recovered: Considered totally unfit and dischargeable by the
Neuropsychiatric Tribunal 11

Evaded 4

Transferred to other hospitals 18

Total percentage of recovered 86.11%

In order to evaluate these data correctly it must be remembered that our unit did not receive the cases directly from the front. The average percentage of recovery from the front centers was still higher—93.6 per cent. Our cases consisted of those evacuated from the first (front) psychiatric units and of those from the rear zone of the army (see Chapter Five). Generally speaking we may assert that the number of mental casualties of the Spanish Republican Army was astonishingly low, and among them the recovery rate was rather higher than those obtained in physical injuries, of course excluding the cases of death. The number of deaths in the group of mental casualties including suicides was 0.18 per cent of the total number of hospitalized cases.

If we turn our attention to the civilian field in order to compare the figures, we shall be surprised by the fact that during the first months of the war there was a notable increase in the admissions to the public psychiatric clinics of Madrid and Barcelona. This fact may be explained by the following two factors: (*a*) the economic collapse that was produced by the downfall of the state determined that many mental patients who had been privately cared for either at home or in private clinics were brought to public institutions; (*b*) the special social conditions prevailing at the beginning of the war occasioned justified fear among a certain number of persons whose sympathies were with the enemy, which precipitated in these either a psychopathic reaction of persecution or the selfish purpose of simulating a depression in order to be interned and protected.

If we eliminate the cases of malingering and take into account only the real mental disturbances observed among the civilians of the largest cities, two facts are notable: (*a*) the relative increase of the schizophrenic reactions (delusions of persecution and of social reform); (*b*) the increase of paraphrenic reactions, or, better, the high incidence of sensory and paranoid delusions in depressed states.

In my opinion both facts may be explained. The first is due to the impossibility for some individuals to continue living in dangerous and hostile surroundings where they must conceal their feelings and face the constant danger of detection. The second is understandable in view of the lack of social support and assistance that the depressed civilian patient has in a war situation. Whereas in peace conditions his family, friends, as well as nurses and doctors can attend to him carefully, supplying continuous reassurance against his feelings of fear and guilt, now everyone is concerned with his own problems and has no time to spare in flattering and pampering the patient. Hence he is more isolated and is left to his self-recrimination and autistic thinking.

Of course, these situations are not found in countries that are conducting a war far beyond their territorial boundaries, but they do occur in the occupied zones of Europe, according to my personal sources of information. As a compensation for the increase of hospitalized cases, a great decrease in the number of visits to the outpatient services of public institutions was noted during the Spanish War and also in London during the present war.

Thus, the comparison between the military and civilian zones yields the following results: (*a*) the neuroses and psychoneuroses are increased in the army and decreased in the civilian population; (*b*) the paranoid (schizophrenic and paraphrenic) syndromes are far more increased among civilians than the military; (*c*) conditions for the restoration of mental casualties, whether neurotic or psychotic, are *better in the army* because of the absence of family interference, the increased feelings of obligation and discipline, the concentration of therapeutic agencies, and the increased authority of the psychiatrist.

DELINQUENTS, CONSCIENTIOUS OBJECTORS, INVALIDS, AND CRIPPLES

Of course, neither delinquents, conscientious objectors, invalids, nor cripples are predominantly psychiatric problems, but the military psychiatrist has something to say about each of them. In regard to delinquents, the military code is, of course, the most severe of all penal codes. Even a slight verbal offense which in civil life would not have serious consequences may subject the offending soldier to a heavy penalty. The views of military leaders who ask for punishment as an example to maintain the strictest discipline must be reconciled with those of the medical experts who know how far an apparently normal man may be driven to behave abnormally under conditions of stress.

Naturally, it would be desirable that a careful psychological and psychiatric examination be made of every delinquent in the army, regardless of rank, but we cannot ask too much on the battlefield, especially during a retreat. I discussed in Chapter Five some of the more frequent misdemeanors committed by enrolled psychopathic personalities. In addition to the proper psychotherapeutic approach to these cases, I venture to state that we achieved good results by transferring most of the delinquents to the *brigadas disciplinarias* and *brigadas de trabajo* ("disciplinary and labor brigades") which were called upon to perform either heavy work such as fortification and hand transportation or asked to provide volunteers for especially dangerous tasks. The jail system and the concentration camp should by all means be avoided; the death penalty for cases of high treason must unfortunately be retained in war conditions, but should be eliminated for all other crimes.

Although there is no such ground for exemption in the Spanish

Army, the problem of conscientious objectors arose as a practical question when students preparing for the priesthood or priests themselves were called up. It was arranged that they should provide religious ministrations as usual and whenever there were too many of them they were transferred to medical services and air-raid-warden posts. It is curious enough that the Anglo-American authorities admit such a category officially, yet, notwithstanding, refuse to discuss openly the conscientious objections of those who do not dare express them. I should prefer to advise the opposite course: not to admit the problem beforehand, but to deal with it in all its extension privately.

A larger problem is that of readapting the crippled and invalided. These men believe that they have given more than was expected to the cause of the war and so claim honorable discharge and life pensions. We decided in favor of the latter but not in favor of the former; in other words we determined that such men should be kept in uniform because we could not afford to risk the loss of their moral influence. Something had to be done to honor these men and at the same time profit from their services. The Chief of the Republican Government and Minister of Defense solved the problem by a decree, according to which they were to be retained during the war as inspectors, managers, administrative officers, teachers, assistants, etc.— according to their capacities—in military institutions of the rear, where they would still profit from the benefits of medical care, vocational guidance, and training.

It may be mentioned that the rebels did something similar with their *caballeros mutilados* ("mutilated gentlemen") whom they kept in special quarters from which they were called for special assignments in the rear zone. Perhaps the reason for such coincidence in practice was that the readaptation and recovery of invalided and crippled workers was very well organized in my country before the war. One of the first international congresses devoted to the matter was held in Madrid under the presidency of Dr. Oller.

I want to emphasize that all invalids require psychiatric assistance in order to readjust their personalities to the new painful conditions of life. There is no use in spending money for orthopedic devices and retraining exercises unless the patient has made up his mind to become a really socially useful citizen in peace as well as in war.

Dr. D'Harcourt, chief military surgeon in charge of this problem, fully agreed that the preliminary requirement of treatment was the exact knowledge of the invalid's personality. How the mutilation affected the person as a whole, what his present aims and ambitions were and how he would try to attain them—all these count in planning subsequent medical, technical, and economic assistance. A certain number of military psychiatrists should specialize in this branch in order to co-operate with the other technical groups engaged in the task of assisting these persons, who constitute the most painful balance of all wars.

CHAPTER EIGHT

MORALE

EXPERIMENTAL CONCEPTION OF MORAL BEHAVIOR

IN JUNE, 1933, I delivered an address to the Congress of the American Association for the Advancement of Science which met in Chicago. The title of that address was the same as of this subheading, and I then presented the results of some years of experimental work in the field. (The complete text was published later in the *Journal of Criminology and Criminal Law*, February, 1934.)

The general conclusion of this work was that all human behavior is directed by three fundamental reactive attitudes, each corresponding to one of the basic emotional patterns: defense—fear; attack—rage; creation—love. The object or unchaining stimulus of such reactions may lie either within the organism or in the external world.

Human behavior, considered from a purely biological or natural angle, is neither moral nor immoral. Moral value is attributed a posteriori whenever behavior is considered from a psychosocial point of view. This means that the ethical value of a given action does not depend merely upon its results, motivations, and aims, but predominantly upon the social frame and the world conception by which we choose to judge it; for instance, Hitler's actions are simultaneously praised and condemned by millions of educated persons.

However, there is a general criterion for the evaluation of social behavior independent of the historical bias in which it is observed. Therefore, I venture to say that human behavior based on fear represents the lowest and oldest form of human morale. When an individual performs or refrains from performing an act because he is afraid of the consequences of behaving otherwise, we cannot expect to profit from the entirety of his mental resources, since his action is not inspired by a primary motivation. In other words, the individual is much more concerned with the avoidance of the punishment than with the result of his work. This is why classical education succeeded in establishing a certain number of social patterns of reaction, but failed miserably to promote human happiness.

When anger motivates the individual, he may utilize his powers fully, but these will be governed by a final destructive aim; happiness can then be attained only through the suffering of someone else. The latter, stimulated to revenge, ultimately will achieve some measure of success: there is no such thing as a small enemy.

Only when an individual behaves under the influence of love is he able to create something that does not presuppose the loss of something else. Only then instead of competition and struggle will there be co-operation and peace. Love means effusion, whereas fear supposes infusion, and rage arouses confusion. Even when a subject falls in love with himself (self-love or narcissism, which, of course, is the worst form of love) he is more profitable to mankind than when he hates himself.

As was stated in the first chapter, the psychological life of man is so complicated that everyone blends more or less of each of these three attitudes of reaction when facing any object or situation. It is for this reason that human actions become so difficult to understand and interpret ethically.

Another general conclusion of the work to which I refer was that there is no radical opposition between the extreme forms of moral behavior. Both best and worst actions can be found in the same man. All we can say is that the social consequences of the individual's actions—and this implies the measure of his responsibility as well—depend predominantly upon (a) the force of his drives; (b) the degree of his intelligence; and (c) his personal influence upon the social group and the social power of the group. Hence, there are persons who can perform neither harm nor good, whatever their purposes may be; but there are others who are always doing harm or good, even if they do not want to do so.

If this is so, and I still believe it is, we may expect great changes in moral standards when a population changes its life from peace to war conditions. We should expect even greater changes if the war were transformed into a revolution.

Such changes cannot be generally qualified as good or bad. Some habits and social trends are changed for the better, others for the worse. By the terms "better" and "worse," I mean, of course, promoting or hindering the *social values* of friendship, brotherhood, sympathy, honesty, generosity, tolerance, cordiality, sincerity, etc. When we consider individuals instead of groups, we shall be surprised to learn, for example, that this man who was cheerful, gentle, and fair behind his counter or desk has turned out to be resentful, mistrustful, jealous, and sarcastic in an advanced post at the front. Conversely, the "black sheep" of the village, coarse, mendacious, and quarrelsome, now becomes, in uniform, quite another person.

Perhaps it was for the same reason that in my blood-transfusion test I found the greatest number of donors among criminals and the least among students of the law. Consequently, the only way to avoid misunderstanding is to speak of war morale as synonymous with determination to achieve military victory over the national enemy, either outside or within the national confines. From this point of view, anything done to accelerate or insure victory is good, and anything done to defer or to endanger it is bad.

GOALS OF WAR MORALE

I shall discuss this topic by paraphrasing the section I wrote in collaboration with Professor Douglas Fryer for his coming book "Military Psychology":

The philosophy of democratic nations includes legal, ethical, and religious standards of pacifism or nonaggression among all individuals and groups. The philosophy of the authoritarian states supports war in competition with other nations. A democracy holds tenaciously to its peacetime habits, inculcated from childhood, even though the conviction may be acceptable that it must change to aggressive national behavior. The authoritarian state is aggressive in peacetime, and war is but an item in its national aggression.

Thus the psychological frame of normal peacetime living in a democracy must be changed to support a war. A reversal of peace-time convictions of personal security must be established so that individual and group survival is recognized as resulting from participation in war.

This change is accomplished by clarifying in detail the wartime goals for individuals and groups in the democracy and by providing participation in training to accomplish them. Democratic goals of war morale follow: (1) There is greater danger and evil for soldier and civilian in total war in escaping from the enemy than in facing him. (2) It is better to obey the requests and laws of official authorities unquestioningly than to evade them, even though in some details they may be recognized as being in error. (3) The enemy is not only bad but weak; he will be defeated eventually regardless of the current appearance of events. (4) Victory will bring all the good, defeat all the evil; victory only comes through individual and group sacrifice of the present to the future. After victory comes peace, prosperity, and happiness—the realization of ideals and a utopian life.

The first goal is to show to civilian and soldier alike by accurate information and illustrations that there is greater danger of being killed, captured, or wounded when passive or submissive than when doing everything possible to destroy the enemy. The soldier must fight to the last whether with his comrades in his own front line or alone behind the enemy's line. The civilian must remain in his community and do everything outlined by authority and everything he can himself devise to hamper the enemy, including complete destruction of his own property when the enemy advances into his community.

To establish the second goal of acceptance of authority the press, radio, and all social organizations are mobilized to teach the value of a universal, controlled, national morale against the enemy during the emergency. Conviction is created through the celebration of historic national events, parades, and patriotic speeches; participation is provided through the formation of civilian defense committees and organizations.

Both of these goals are represented in an equation prepared for Republican Spain: a pacifist is a deserter today, an enemy tomorrow; he should be treated accordingly.

The third goal, superiority over the enemy, is established in soldier and civilian alike by the development and maintenance of patriotic attitudes and feelings of pride in national accomplishments. Pride is cultivated through the exhibition of films of great historic events, ceremonies in honor of heroes, decorations for distinctive participation in the war effort, display of flags, exhibits of devastating military equipment, and broadcasts of war programs.

The fourth goal, a utopia after the war, is more difficult to establish since individuals are reluctant to accept promises of future benefits in return for present sacrifices. Political opinions and beliefs may differ so much among the citizens of the nation that it is almost impossible to find a concrete postwar program that will satisfy the majority. Where several governments are allied, this is even more difficult. In order to remove such differences, a readjustment in the government is usually advisable, such as was accomplished by the national government in England and a political body of all factions in France and in Republican Spain. In this way all social groups within the nation are brought to feel that their ideas of social organization or formulas for improvement are being considered for future application. Meetings of scientific societies and social clubs can be encouraged to prepare for reconstruction after the war. But for the present, owing to the emergency, everyone must agree to forget his own desires and increase his obligations to society. "Sacrifice is unavoidable for the conquest of victory and future happiness," "What seems to be evil now will prove to be good later," are some of the themes embroidering the goal. A declaration of war aims acceptable to the greatest number serves as a utopian rallying point, such as those made by Wilson in 1918, by Negrin in 1938, and by Roosevelt and Churchill in 1941.

Whether the individuals or groups ever get or can get what they want is an untimely question in the war emergency. Intelligent individuals and groups with high war morale will recognize this and will look to the future for its stimulating effect on morale even though they may be convinced that the future after a war can never be so good as the past just before it. Once the war situation is recognized as inevitable this goal is acceptable.

HOW TO INTEGRATE MORALE

In spite of the fact that wars of today are total ones, a difference exists between the conditions of morale in the military combat zones and those in the civilian rear. It may be said a priori that morale is usually higher at the army zone because of (a) the selection of combatants, since only those men physically and mentally fit are accepted; (b) the accumulation of military might—guns, tanks, airplanes, etc.—which gives confidence of invincibility; (c) the existence of a feeling of fellowship and co-operation which makes the individual feel protected and encouraged by his group.

At the rear, conversely, all the weak and sick congregate; cowards frequently succeed in remaining there also, more or less camouflaged; there is far more heterogeneity of opinion and relaxation of community boundaries, and enemy propaganda can be spread more easily.

There are many concrete examples to show that the rear is, at the last moment, the weak point which may finally crush the morale of the combatants. This happened in Germany in 1918 and was repeated in Republican Spain in 1939. Most soldiers are better able to endure their own suffering than the thought that by continuing to fight they prolong and increase the suffering of those they love. If they are deprived of news, they believe the worst; if news from home is too laconic, they resent the censorship; and if the news comes uncensored, they realize that their families long to have them back. This force, drawing them back to the rear, may become more effective in undermining army morale than the pressing force of the enemy ahead.

Conversely, those in the rear are usually more anxious about what is happening to their particularly beloved combatants, sons, husbands, brothers, fathers, or sweethearts than about the dangers of invasion or slavery. Because the prospect of the national future in the event of defeat is not clearly grasped by many citizens in all its magnitude, they worry mainly: "Where is he?" "Is he dead or alive?"

The problem is, then, how to integrate morale in such a way that each zone may reinforce the other. I previously advanced the idea that special attention must be devoted to the bridge between the two zones, since there they overlap and mix despite all possible attempts at prevention. In the case of the United States, this bridge is represented by the coast zones of both oceans.

The most important organization for maintaining war morale must accordingly be located in the bridge zone, and, since the mixture cannot be avoided, it must be properly controlled. The primary caution is carefully to watch the feminine element living in or transferred to the zone, since this element is the carrier of private, uncensored news to both sides. A second measure is to distribute a sufficient number of reporting agents in such zones to detect those persons likely to talk too much or to spread ill-advised rumors. Fighting against rumors is as important as fighting against the enemy, but sometimes it is advisable, from the standpoint of high military strategy, to spread false rumors (counterrumors) to disorient enemy spies.

A third very important measure is the control of correspondence. Since the censorship is located, or should be, at this intermediate zone, it is advisable to have printed instructions, to be delivered only privately and verbally to those who are going to write across the barrier in either direction. Such instructions must refer especially to the following points: (*a*) avoid any information that would be used by the enemy if he could read the letter; (*b*) do not upset your beloved relatives by explaining your sufferings or misfortunes; try to help them by telling them the best possible news, since it would not do any good to increase their anxiety about you; (c) try to advance the date of the letter three or four days in order that it may seem more recent when received; (d) include all possible smiling snapshots, and do not forget to tell a good new joke, if possible.

As for the important point of transferring persons from the rear to the army zone in order to entertain the troops, and vice versa, to send some hero back to the rear from the front, it is always advisable to do so, and it usually works satisfactorily provided proper selection is made of the persons. In the Spanish War, however, we found it better to organize special broadcasts to the front, and also from the front to the rear, rather than to transfer the artists.

The most important condition, however, for raising the morale of the whole nation is the assurance of clear and concrete information as to what is at stake in the war and what everyone risks in the event of defeat. Such information cannot be based on brilliant words and abstract assertions, but must rest on solid facts. Every citizen, civilian or soldier, must know what the course of his life will be if the enemy wins. Such information should not be conveyed by histrionic politicians or by paid employees of the ministry of war. It will be far better received if delivered by well-known scientists. Almost all the university professors on the Spanish Republican side volunteered for such assignments, and that is one of the reasons why they are now in exile. Never in history did the best brains of a nation come into such close contact with the population and the army as in the recent Spanish War. They succeeded in explaining to the dullest soldiers and civilians what was going on in the world, and why they were called upon to fight. They even succeeded in convincing the people that immediate death was preferable to postponed death plus eternal ignominy. Because the citizens have a great respect for scientists and know that they will not lie, men of science have a tremendous psychological value and consequently should be used not merely in their strictly technical capacities but also in accordance with their human powers of persuasion.

PERSUASION, SUGGESTION, AND COERCION

I have stated that whenever the population *fears* the consequences of defeat, *hates* the enemy leaders responsible for the war, and *loves* the consequences of victory, morale is at its peak.

There are three means of directing human behavior: appeal to reason (persuasion), appeal to affection (suggestion), and appeal to duty (compulsion). The first is to be used to the maximal extent by the most eminent and creditable men of the country, and, in the first place, as already emphasized, by highly qualified scholars and scientists. The second is to be employed by the artists, especially the writers, and the priests. The third will be in the hands of the official government and will be regulated by law and policy.

Psychotherapists assert that neither pure persuasion, suggestion, compulsion nor prohibition is sufficiently effective when a man is called upon to resist powerful subconscious forces or his own pressing drives. Three competitive psychoanalytic schools have tried to work with one single weapon of this group to readjust psychopathic individuals: the Freudians, who convey to the patient, coldly and neutrally, the greatest possible amount of information; the Jungians, who create in him the belief that he possesses new and boundless energies (and hence work predominantly in the field of mythical suggestion); and the Adlerians, who face the patient severely and recall to him his social duties, warning him that he will never attain peace and satisfaction until he behaves correctly. Each of these schools has its adherents, achieving success with one particular kind of personality, failing with others. The clever psychotherapist knows how, in each case, to combine the proper amount of information (persuasion), inspiration (suggestion), and admonition (compulsion or coercion) to achieve the best results.

Enthusiasm for fighting is not sufficient, because although more desirable than indifference, it is subject to sudden changes. *Conviction* is necessary to produce the cold determination to prosecute the fight when the enthusiasm is over. *Submission to strong discipline* is also required, and constitutes the emphasis on the duty concept.

Because of the enormous diffusion of political ideologies all over the world, there is scarcely a person who does not have his own political philosophy, and almost everyone, therefore, requests information or discussion about the *reasons* for fighting. Not to speak about these things is as silly as not to speak about sexual problems to adolescents: they will find their way in spite of the censure of the parents. So the people will make up their minds in spite of the silence of the political leaders when the latter refuse to discuss fundamentals. The best way to convey suggestion is in the form of "rationalization." The Germans are undoubtedly the masters of this. Their use of apparently logical principles minutely developed serves to conceal the falsehood of their premises. This procedure is the same one at work in paranoiac brains, and it is admittedly difficult to demonstrate the error in the assumptions of a paranoiac.

This kind of suggestive propaganda must be presented as printed material and graphic illustrations. More people rally to the exactness of a graph than to the truth of words, although all of us know how easy it is to use statistics to distort facts.

Posters and cartoons properly drawn can also have a tremendous suggestive power. The comic touch is superior to the tragic tone. So, for instance, the enemy should not be pictured as a monster or as a fierce animal, since such a portrayal is more likely to frighten than to encourage the average citizen. On the contrary, he must be ridiculed and scorned. A very brief slogan, if possible in rhyme, increases the effect. Russians and Spaniards used this form of suggestive propaganda skillfully, so it is no wonder that the first prize of an international contest for the best cartoon for the victory of the Allied nations was won by a Spanish artist, Renau, formerly director of fine arts in Madrid, and now a Mexican citizen.

A good example of this kind of propaganda is shown by the stimulating effects of a cartoon entitled "A Man Who Never Can Be" (*"Franco nunca será Franco,"* i. e., "Franco can never be frank," a play on words, since the word "franco" in Spanish means honest and sincere). The Spanish *"Führer"* was pictured behind a wall, standing on a platform sustained by German, Italian, Portuguese, and Moorish soldiers; his legs were trembling, and his hand convulsively grasped the platform as his head appeared just above the wall and he cried: *"Arriba Espana!"* ("Heil Spain!") Spain was a dying bull lying at the bottom of the drawing and supporting all the described scenery. The wall itself was composed of a multitude of generals, businessmen, and bishops. The red blood of the bull, spreading between the yellow wheat and the purple skies, formed the Spanish Republican flag which was finally raised by the winds of freedom and democracy. This composition possessed all the qualities of symbolism, humor, realism, and what the Germans call *Anforderungscharakter* (i. e., inciting force). Everyone who looked at it felt stimulated and pleased with its effect.

A word may be said about the third factor—coercion. I am not attempting to deny its value, but I wish to emphasize that it has far less than that of the other two factors, despite appearances to the contrary. If it becomes necessary to employ this last force by laws either of compulsion or of prohibition supported by extremely severe penalties, *it is always preferable to apply such factors openly rather than secretly*. The Germans, for instance, do not conceal the shooting of their hostages, and that is how they succeed in ruling over hundreds of millions of people who hate them. The government must not act in secrecy and has no need to proceed in disguise, as is the custom of professional bandits.

There is only one way to avoid as much as possible the use of such coercive brakes: to insure that the average citizen understands and approves the sacrifices he is called upon to make. This in turn will be easily attained whenever those who ask such sacrifices are the first to make them themselves. So, for instance, deprivation such as rationing should be shared not merely by the people but also by the authorities; the only exceptions will be determined not by the social or official hierarchy but by the type and intensity of the exertion that each is called upon to perform. During the Spanish War, for instance, any girl working in a munitions factory received more food than I, because she needed an extra ration for her muscular efforts, and I did not.

Equality and fairness in the endurance of danger and suffering constitute perhaps the most important factors for sustaining the morale of a people during the hardest conditions of the war. This fact has been thoroughly understood by all the famous warriors and leaders in history. It is a matter of justice to admit that Hitler is aware of it as well and extracts therefrom the maximum of advantage.

MEASUREMENTS OF MORALE AMONG CIVILIANS AND SOLDIERS

No one is defeated until he admits it to himself. As long as the fighting purpose is maintained there is always a chance, even under the worst material conditions, to continue the struggle to achieve victory. Hence, the periodic measurement of the will to fight or of the war morale of the nation is as important as the attainment of a high war production. History provides many examples to show how the decay of morale is relatively independent of physical exhaustion and of the strategic position of the army at the moment.

Two kinds of approaches may be used to gain insight into the collective morale: observation and experiment. The first may be direct or indirect. The second may be accomplished by means of verbal or motor (performance) test devices. My experience favors the use of indirect observation and the collective performance tests.

Peacetime methods of examination of public opinion fail, of course, during war, because the laws for national defense prevent anyone from expressing frankly his inner feelings when these do not coincide with what is officially expected. Thus, interviews, questionnaires, and discussions—as well as verbal tests—may elicit some information as to the mental and emotional state but will fail to provide reliable data concerning the purposes and decisions of the group, i. e., the determination to prosecute the war.

To compensate for such deficiencies during the late Spanish War, I essayed some means of indirect observation of collective morale in the civil population and in the army. Following the line of previous investigations (see "New Directions in Testing Affectivity," *Proceedings of the Ninth International Congress of Psychology,* Yale University) I first used statistical data as an index, such as, for instance, the amount of beverages sold, the number of people attending public entertainments, the percentage of volunteers registered at the different services, the number of voluntary blood donations, and the amounts of money collected during street solicitation campaigns conducted in especially selected experimental areas of the city.

Very soon I devised steps for beginning experimental research on the matter. One of the first attempts consisted of the deliberate loss of special ration cards in which the names of the owners could easily be substituted by those of the finders. Advertisements in the journals requested the return of the cards. The number *not* returned was supposed to increase in the ratio of the decrease in morale. The experiment failed because of lack of co-operation of the employees controlling the offices of the Board of Nutrition (Comissaría de Alimentació).

A second attempt in the same direction was made in the advertising page of the journals by publishing the following announcement: "Young, handsome person is wanted to assist old foreign lady and eventually to accompany her abroad. Please write to box number 1276." All applicants were asked to send their personal records and it was expected that the number of replies would be in proportion to the desire to escape from the hardships of the war situation. When the experiment was at its climax I was informed that it was much easier to obtain direct information about the percentages of people deserting from their posts, asking for exit permits, complaining of infirmity, or applying for social assistance. All these data were in different hands, and it seemed to me almost impossible to have them at my disposal, but I was wrong; they proved to be excellent indicators of the morale at any given moment.

INDICES OF MORALE

When the war was already in its third year I realized that another means of gaining insight into the morale of the population and army had been disregarded: the analysis of the spontaneous topics of conversation and the reactions of the listeners to the so-called exploring jokes broadcast by the radio. Also, the speed with which artificially fabricated rumors, favorable and adverse, circulate is a good index of the state of morale in a given environment. Summing up all the experience collected throughout the war, and also in exile, I think it may be worth while to cite the principal signs of good and bad war morale as judged from behavior in relation to events.

High war morale is expressed by (*a*) high enlistment of volunteers in combatant services; (*b*) high financial contribution in the street campaigns; (*c*) overflow of letters, projects, suggestions, and inventions spontaneously addressed to the official agencies in order to increase the striking power of the national army against the enemy; (*d*) exhibition of all kinds of insignia, flags, pictures, and military emblems in the rear zone; (*e*) large sales of patriotic songs, stories, records, and souvenirs; (*f*) spontaneous cheers and applause for army units, propaganda films, political representatives, etc.; (*g*) optimistic jokes and humorous or depreciatory slogans about the enemy; (*h*) cessation of rumors; (*i*) complete credit and faith in the official news and reliance upon the rulers of the nation; (*j*) intense planning of postwar reconstruction projects.

Mediocre war morale or the weakening of the desirable high level, already described, is shown by (*a*) increase of allegations and arguments *legally* to elude war risks and obligations; (*b*) increase of the tendency *legally* to secure individual ownership, by means of speculation, monopoly, conversion of bills into goods and chattels, etc.; (c) increase of discussions concerning war aims and strategy with bitter criticism of government policy; (d) increase of institutions for relief and of all the agencies operating with superstition and magic beliefs; (e) progressive indifference to war literature and art; (f) lack of attendance at reviews or parades of the armed forces; (g) jokes about the defects and inadequacies of one's own side; (h) reluctance to accept the official news, and rapid diffusion of rumors concerning big losses or concealed disagreements among the chief commanders or between them and the political authorities; (i) tolerance of the apparently candid assertion that the war is silly and will not come to a victorious end, since everybody will lose in it (this being the first phase of the pacifists' and negotiators' attack); (j) appearance of war neuroses as a problem in the fighting forces.

Assuming that the decay of the national morale progresses still further, new and alarming signs may appear as the heralds of defeat. Such signs are almost always observed first in the rear zone, and then they infiltrate toward the military zone, promoting the collapse of the fighters. We may summarize then as follows: (a) continuous decrease of the production curve in spite of the increased severity of the measures decreed to enlarge it; (b) unjustified increase of prices of goods and merchandise because traders and merchants do not want to exchange them for money but prefer to store them; (c) total drop in the field of private suggestions for winning the war; (d) complete disinterestedness concerning the patriotic speeches, parades, and affairs for war propaganda; (e) reluctance and passive resistance against the latest official dispositions concerning any aspect whatsoever of the national life; (f) appearance of pacifist labels, placards, and handwritten slogans ("Stop the war," "We want peace," etc.); (g) increase of spontaneous declinations or resignations from directing posts, giving rise to increasing disorganization and stagnation in bureaucratic activities; (h) increase in suicides and delinquency; (i) increase in the number of war neurotics in the rear, and relative increase in mental casualties among the officers and commanders;

(*j*) unjustified increase in the number of prisoners lost by the military units; (*k*) appearance of homesickness among the troops. This is a peculiar kind of craving which may cause combatants to desert their posts in order to return to their homes and be hidden by their relatives, waiting for the end of the fighting; more than a desertion, this fugue is to be considered a *re*insertion into the core of family life, because the subject has regressed to his infantile level of behavior and wants to be cheered and protected, instead of himself to be the protector.

MEASURES OF INDIVIDUAL FIGHTING POWER

Where there is a will, there is not always a way. More than one citizen longs to become a national hero but fails in his ambition because of lack of opportunity, intelligence, or endurance. What really matters in war situations is not so much what an individual intends as what he actually accomplishes. Hence it is desirable to have an objective index of the mental power or fitness of the combatants at any given moment. To what extent this power is determined by constitutional trends, by the incentive of praise, by the sense of duty, by the action of some exciting substance, etc., is quite immaterial provided only that such power exists.

I have always been struck by the importance that military commanders give to the martial appearance of their troops on parade. They insist repeatedly that the soldiers move, salute, and march with a special uniformity and with almost mechanical accuracy, as if they were nothing more than automatons. General Moltke even said: "Let me see how two armies march along the road and I will forecast which of the two will win the battle." In order to achieve such muscular control, all armies devote considerable time and energy to the physical training of the recruits, teaching them especially how to *stand* like real soldiers; I should even venture to say that the differences in the manner of standing and marching are the most essential differences between civilians and military men.

When reading about the motor theory of consciousness, and especially when thinking about the viewpoint of dynamic psychology (or "topology," as Kurt Lewin calls it), I concluded that there is not only an art of expression but also the possibility of a science of expression, and that a careful observation of the postures and gestures of any individual may do much to reveal his inner attitudes, despite a voluntary intention to simulate or to dissimulate. If the individual intentions may be conceived as *in*-tensions, and these internal tensions are reflected at the muscular level, there is no doubt that the care with which the army leaders endeavor to obtain a perfect distribution of the muscular tensions in the bodies of the soldiers is fully justified. Of course, all the attempts that have been made in the fields of physiognomy, chirology, and graphology, as well as those made by painters and movie producers during the era of the silent films, are to be understood in the same way. Even the James-Lange theory would be enriched by such a point of view. The same is true of the benefits of occupational therapy in mental disease: the performance of new movements would destroy the distorted patterns of muscular reaction that have become fixed and rigid in the individual, thus creating the possibility of the corresponding change in his frame of mind.

Since I thought about this in 1935, I decided to create some device for gaining insight into the skeleton of character through the analysis of the uncontrolled muscular tensions of the individual. While I worked with the method of the motor expression of Luria to detect the sincerity of testimony, my belief was further reinforced. Using a certain kind of monotometer as a lie detector (described in my book, *Psicología Jurídica,* published in 1932) I was impressed by the fact that the length of movements tended throughout to decrease in the inhibited subjects and to increase in the excited subjects, irrespective of the content of the questions or the nature of the verbal reply.

Then the Spanish War began in July, 1936, and all this mental rumination was ended by more urgent and pressing tasks. In June, 1937, the problem of selecting the applicants for the School of Military Aviation at Barcelona led me to the construction of a device that was to measure the accuracy of the kinesthetic perception of space—the axistereometer. Working with this I obtained unexpected results which recalled to me my old preoccupation and caused me to discover what I denominated as the general principle of psychomyokinesis. Before I came to this point, a summarized description of the instrument and its initial results in testing the flying candidates seems necessary.

THE AXISTEREOMETER

The instrument consists of a cylindrical stalk made of brass (aximeter), about 60 centimeters long and 2 centimeters in diameter, calibrated in millimeters. Lengthwise, slide manually two hoops: the superior is previously fixed at will a certain distance from the near end; the inferior, more easily movable, serves to measure the distance thus limited (Fig. 1, p. 139) and remains in the place marked by the subject, no matter what the position of the stalk may be. The latter can be rotated and may be fixed in position every 45 degrees of the five basic planes: horizontal, sagittal, vertical, and right and left obliques, permitting in all forty measurements.

In order to gain this mobility, the stalk is inserted through its central extremity in a double multiple body. The earlier model of this body has been recently improved by Professor Calcagno (La Plata University) but details of its construction are not essential for grasping the facts we are about to emphasize. Instead of fixing the apparatus across a socle to a rectangular table, the Calcagno model is provided with a heavy removable tripod within which the stalk may be fixed at the most convenient height through a pressing screw.

The subject is seated, preferably on a rotating stool, and placed in front of the instrument in such a way that his xiphoid process is at the same level as the central extremity of the aximeter and on the same horizontal axis. The experiment begins by obtaining the measures in the vertical plane first, using the dominant hand of the individual. The instructions are as follows: "Let us see the accuracy with which you are capable of measuring a distance on this stalk without the aid of your sight. Please take this hoop (inferior), hold it in your fingers, and move it slowly three times, up and down and vice versa, between the base of the stalk and this top (superior) hoop, so as to acquire a true impression of the distance existing between the two." The examiner demonstrates what he means. "Now I shall interpose this screen, take away the upper hoop, and request you to take the lower hoop between your thumb and middle fingers and replace it at the height the upper ring was, i. e., try to measure the same distance. You will immediately repeat this operation until you have made three trials, thus allowing us to average your errors."

The experimenter must insure that the subject maintains the correct position during the measuring, note in the corresponding graph the results obtained, and then say: "Now the stalk will turn and be replaced in different positions, but you will endeavor in all of them to replace the hoop three times in the same position, i. e., at the same distance from the base of the stalk."

Before obtaining the measures in a new plane or with the other hand, the subject is allowed to renew visually the impression of the distance he is to measure. After the vertical comes the sagittal, then the horizontal, and finally the oblique series of measurements. The obliques are to be performed with the hand belonging to the hemispace in which the point of the stalk lies; of course, when this is rotating along the sagittal plane the measures are successively obtained with the right and left hand.

In order to avoid weariness of attention, a pause of five minutes is advisable at the end of the investigation in the sagittal plane; and if we are dealing with psychopathic subjects or with persons suffering from stereognostic disturbances it is better to complete the test in a second session. The most important rule to be observed is that of avoiding displacements of the subject's body during the execution of the test.

RESULTS WITH FLIERS

When I began the systematic testing of the candidates for military aviation at my laboratory of the Psychotechnical Institute of Barcelona, my intention was to correlate the results of the standard labyrinthine examination and the axistereometric tests. A high positive correlation between these data was expected, and it was also presumed that the frequency curve of the errors in the axistereometric test would correspond to the classical Gaus model. Neither of these two suppositions, however, was confirmed by the facts. Each individual possessed a peculiar stereokinetic profile and had particular diameters in which he committed plus or minus errors that did not correspond to the average. Fig. 2 shows one such profile in the five fundamental planes (the dotted lines correspond to the records of the left hand). It is easy to observe how specifically irregular, but constant, such shapes are in the left horizontal and oblique and the right oblique diameters. Thinking that such differences in kinetic estimation of distances might be related with a psychological or characterological factor, I endeavored to compare the stereograms belonging to groups of aviators who possessed the same type of personality (according to the Rorschach, Bernreuter, and Jung-Rosanoff tests) and those of subjects with peculiar modalities of abnormal personality. Consequently, I concluded that some central trends of character, expressed in the predominance of a fundamental attitude of reaction, led the individual to perform with unusual facility the sets of movements securing the satisfaction of the involved purposes and to perform with great difficulty those opposed to them.

I also realized that the constancy of the figures obtained by left-hand testing in right-handed individuals was greater than obtained with the right hand. Dr. Werner Wolff was working in my institute at that time, and so I related this fact with his own view that the entire left side of the body is better able to express the unconscious life, while the right side is more closely linked with consciousness and so is more prone to variation. When I tried to explain the mean-

FIGURE 1.

The axistereometer.

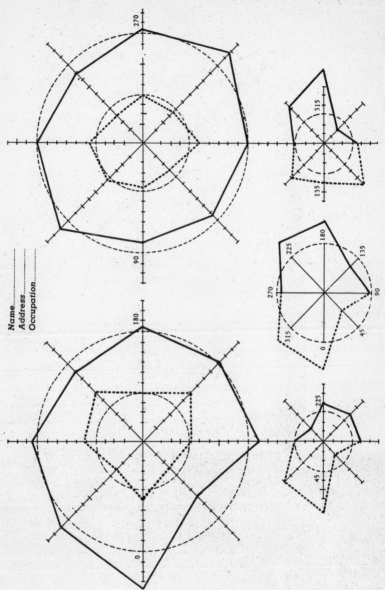

FIGURE 2.

Axistereometric tracings.

ing of the abnormal shapes in the stereograms with such criteria, the correlation between this interpretation and the subject's clinical psychological history was almost perfect.

No wonder, then, that when the Spanish War was over I was desirous to prosecute this line of investigation at the Maudsley Hospital of London, profiting from the help of the Society for Protection of Science and Learning and the kindness of Professors Charles Myers, Mapother, and Aubrey Lewis. As a result of such work, in October, 1939, I presented a preliminary paper to the Royal Society of Medicine entitled, "A New Method of Exploring the Conative Trends of Personality (Myokinetic Psychodiagnosis)." (This paper was published in the *Proceedings of the Society,* Section of Psychiatry, in February, 1940, pp. 172-94.) Unfortunately, I could not correct the proofs, since I left the country in the interval to go to Argentina, and so the statistical figures and charts contain some typographical errors.

Once I was settled in Argentina the investigation was resumed, this time with the invaluable help of Drs. R. Melgar, C. Coronel, and Ortiz Gonzales (the last has published his thesis in the University of Chile, *El Psicodiagnóstico Mioquinético de Mira y Lopez,* 1942). Experimenting with more than a thousand normal and abnormal subjects (delinquents, psychopaths, etc.) we believe that we are now in possession of a new principle and technique of research on mental fitness which is especially useful for psychiatrists operating in emergency conditions, and therefore very applicable to military psychiatry.

THE PRINCIPLE OF PSYCHOMYOKINESIS

As anticipated a few pages earlier, the principle of psychomyokinesis is implicit in the work of Gall, Darwin, Chevreuil, Mosso, and the more recent concepts of Crepieux, Klages, W. Stern, Lewin, Downey, Wolff, Allport, Vernon, and E. Strauss. These and many other authors have insisted on the importance of the expressive movements for gaining insight into the peculiarities of the individual tem-

perament and character (see, for example, the book of Allport and
Vernon published in 1933, *Studies in Expressive Movement*). Storch
proposed the term *myopsyche* to designate the functional division of
the individual which stores the energies securing the execution of
the fundamental purposes of the organism, and, according to the
views of Watson, even the most simple thought cannot be performed
without altering in some way the muscular patterns. In his book,
Sinn der Sinne, E. Strauss writes the following enlightening remarks:

> Can we seriously say that the movement is in the muscle? Of course
> it is not; nor is it in the nerves, in the ganglion cells, in the cerebral
> convolutions, in the pyramidal tract, or in any other tract of the pallidal
> or cerebellar system. No more is it in the passively moved parts. What
> does the expression *a movement, the movement,* or *the movements* really
> mean? With what right are movements to be considered something me-
> chanical? Muscular contraction is a process within the organism, but
> movement itself is a function of the relations between the individual and
> his world.

Thus, the general principle of psychomyokinesis, in terms of which
my myokinetic psychodiagnosis becomes understandable, may be
stated:

> Psychological space is not neutral; all movements executed by the
> individual—either purposefully or not—acquire a peculiar meaning ac-
> cording to the direction in which they are performed. (For instance, in
> our present occidental culture, a movement accomplished from left to
> right has a progressive coloring, whereas the same movement when per-
> formed from right to left seems regressive.)

> All mental activity may be considered as a succession of acts implying
> a succession of *postural* changes; *whenever the mental equilibrium is dis-
> torted, such distortion must in some way be detectable in the individual's
> movements,* and it will appear evident to the degree that we succeed in
> eliminating any voluntary attempt at momentary compensation.

> Consequently, if we ask an individual to perform small oscillatory
> movements in the fundamental directions of space, *without visual control,*

the observed shifts will be significant of the predominant muscular patterns, and so will provide insight as to his fundamental attitudes of
reaction [see Appendix for the technique of the test which applies this
principle].

CHAPTER NINE

MENTAL HYGIENE

MENTAL HYGIENE UNDER WAR CONDITIONS

THERE is no doubt that work in mental hygiene must be increased in war conditions. Even in time of peace the problems of mental hygiene are not sufficiently attended to by the official powers. Dr. A. Watters recently pointed out that "about one fourth of the cities over a hundred thousand and almost two thirds of those between fifty thousand and a hundred thousand population have no psychiatric facilities for children or adults"; of course, this means that they do not have a mental hygiene organization either. Watters' report referred to the United States in 1942, where about two million persons are victims of formal mental disorder of such a nature as to be statistically covered; we may imagine how much worse the conditions must be in other countries not possessing so high a standard of living.

Thus the nation at war faces not only the danger of an increase of individual mental disorders but also the danger of the appearance of *collective mental disorders;* to prevent them is the task of psychiatrists, working as mental hygienists in the central offices directing the public, civil, and military life. A distinction must be made between the work done to produce good war morale and that to further mental hygiene: it is granted that the first facilitates the second, but the latter is far more extensive and complicated. We have often observed, for example, how mental disorders have affected with peculiar preference some of the men with the highest war morale and the greatest eagerness to fight the enemy. The problems of war mental hygiene cannot and must not be solved by the morale branch of the General Staff, although it is undeniable that the closest collaboration should be assured between this branch and the board of army mental hygiene services, directed by prominent psychiatrists.

This board must also work intimately with the agencies securing the hygiene of the army, since we have come to a point where it is no longer possible to establish a sharp distinction between somatic and psychic hygienic measures.

PSYCHOSOMATIC CRITERIA

The theory of the "double aspect" of human life must be accepted by medical men, and as Sandor Rado cleverly points out in an article about traumatic neuroses (*Psychosomatic Medicine,* No. 4, 1942) the differences between somatic and psychic disorders are more dependent upon the method of examination than upon the nature of the underlying process: from *inspection* we obtain a collection of abnormal physical signs, from *introspection* (or, better, *heterospection*) we bring to light a number of abnormal mental experiences, the first serving to establish the existence of a somatic and the second of a psychic disturbance in the same man. I am all the more convinced of the correctness of the psychosomatic criterion, since I am accustomed to see how all mental disorders are manifest in terms of spatial shifts in the M.P.D.

The study of the proper feeding of a military unit camping in a new territory is important for the prevention of physical as well as mental disorders. So is the arrangement of the entertainments, the planning of the lectures, and, even, the distribution of assignments within each military group. Because of this conviction I made all possible efforts to give basic notions of mental hygiene to all the military physicians, and tried to instill in them the belief that wherever the military commander plays the part of the primitive father in the recruit's mind, the military physician should try to perform the part of the primitive mother—but, of course, a mother knowing the fundamentals of psychoanalysis and so complementing instead of opposing the influence of the father.

There is another reason why the regimental physicians should be the mainstay of the mental hygiene work of the units, and that is their knowledge of the constitutional background of the men under their care. Only by taking into account this constitutional factor can we obviate many mistakes in judging human behavior and in dealing with the men.

From this point of view I would be strongly in favor of a quick generalization of Sheldon's and Stevens' typology, since it gives, in my opinion, reliable hints for predicting how far a man will endure a given task without failing. Working in conditions of emergency I simply recommended to my pupils that they pick those men possessing a "constitutional" hand (the left in right-handed persons and vice versa), which shifts slightly upward in the vertical lineograms of the M.P.D., and a "leading" or "dominating" hand (the right in right-handed persons and vice versa) well controlled in the horizontals and shifting slightly forward in the sagittals.

Such men are a priori better equipped to resist the action of adverse or unfavorable influences, since, according to the interpretation of the M.P.D. they possess excellent vitality, good aggressiveness, and perfect voluntary control. It is from among such men that leaders and volunteers for especially difficult military tasks should be chosen.

I regret that concrete data concerning the correlation between the results of the M.P.D. and those of practical life cannot be cited now because I lost the material collected in the Spanish War and I am not authorized to publish the most recent findings obtained in Argentina by working with civilian fliers, students at the university, and professional surgeons. However, the technique of performing the first part of the M.P.D., as described in the Appendix, is so easy that any physician can experiment with his own acquaintances and relatives and convince himself how closely related are the myokinetic (geometric, psychic, and somatic) images of the individual and his life achievements, so that new support is lent to the psychosomatic criterion in dealing with problems in this field.

COLLABORATION OF THE PSYCHIATRIST WITH CIVIL AND MILITARY AUTHORITIES

As previously stated, war means, more or less, the dissolution of privacy and the interference of the state in all individual activities, which are then organized and submitted to the highest aim of national defense. Individuals are thus regrouped into special working units either in offices and factories in the rear or in ships and army quarters at the fronts. This means the necessity for working out a new *Lebensplan* ("living program") for them. The difficulty is that although people are biologically and psychologically different, the way in which they are to live must be uniform. Thus psychiatrists must provide for the introduction of all the possible variations in such collective-living programs as to fit them for individual peculiarities. Professor Albert Einstein once wrote that the secret of human happiness lies in a perfect distribution of periods of work, amusement, and rest. Unfortunately, war imposes too much work and too little amusement and rest. Much can be done, nevertheless, to secure the most profit from the pauses in fighting and working. According to the cultural background and interests of men, they should be organized into groups to attend all possible types of entertainments and amusements that do not exhaust, demoralize, or excite them too much. From this point of view the necessity becomes evident to promote all kinds of sports and contests; to secure good artistic performances, lectures, radio addresses, etc.; and to regulate the time distribution and location of such activities in a way that allows their enjoyment without the waste of time and energy.

Special care must be taken with the functioning of bars, cabarets, gambling places, and all the agencies that offer artificial happiness at high prices. People are too fond of them not to miss their absence: they must therefore be controlled rather than suppressed. Special observers must be placed in such locales and instructed to report excesses both on the part of the patrons and the employees. Of course, much of such artificial enjoyment is sought only when natural sources of satisfaction are lacking. Therefore, special emphasis must be placed on securing adequate periodic psychological contact of combatants with those people for whom they particularly care. Such contacts, of course, can only be established by correspondence, pictures, and radio. During the Spanish War we recommended special short-wave transmissions, from nodal points in the country, of "concrete news" to those living abroad or far away; all the speeches were, of course, previously supervised, and only people who were very popular and well known in their localities were chosen. It was simply amazing how our men became interested in these auditions and renounced other more dangerous sources of satisfaction in the nightly hours that were devoted to them.

Psychiatrists are also called upon to co-operate with civilian and military authorities in securing good reading matter (newspapers, magazines, and books) and in suppressing the spread of nasty, degrading literature in the army. This is a really important problem which must be dealt with very carefully and with a fine psychological touch. It is equally important that psychiatrists and morale officers be ever alert to discover men with special entertaining abilities and to insure that they make suitable use of their talents.

As far as possible psychiatrists must encourage all forms of round-table conferences and informal meetings where a free discussion of topics of collective interest may take place under the supervision of the mental hygienist or the morale officer. These discussions afford an excellent occasion for judging the state of morale, for knowing the minds of the men, and for teaching the general principles of mental hygiene. What is still more important, they serve to create good fellowship between persons of different military ranks and units and so forward one of the fundamental aims of mental hygiene: to make the individual feel supported by all his comrades, and to regard all the men in the army as his comrades.

IMPORTANCE OF GOOD FELLOWSHIP IN THE ARMY

As just stated, the creation of good fellowship is perhaps the most important aim of all military mental hygiene work. Psychiatrists must fight against the tendency toward encystment and isolation of individuals from their groups, as well as against the creation of small cliques within larger groups. The army must not be conceived as a series of juxtaposed units or of superimposed ranks of men, but as a single living superperson, endowed with all the forces of all the inhabitants of the nation and charged with the noble mission of representing them at a given historical moment.

All military men must remember that they are of equal importance to the country, although for the special requirements of their tasks they were endowed with different amounts of physical and moral power. What is important in the evaluation of a man is not what he is asked to do but how he does it; hence, a good soldier is far better than a poor corporal, and even the commander in chief must not feel superior to the most humble recruit if the latter performs all his obligations. Herein lies, of course, the most difficult part of the problem: how to secure blind obedience to orders emanating from the superiors and yet make the various ranks of the army experience the feelings of equality and camaraderie. In the measure that this difficulty is solved, the different army organizations will acquire a soul and live beyond the limits of their mechanical strength.

Much can be gained in this direction if psychiatrists succeed in convincing military leaders that they are merely invested, by their titles and ranks, with *actority* but that they must acquire their *authority* (prestige) by gaining it in daily contact with the men under their command. Orders will be far better obeyed if those who give them are credited with being efficient and capable commanders; this is something that cannot be gained by issuing a decree or assumed from the stripes and stars of the uniforms. Anyone can be an *actor*, but only those possessing intelligence and inspiration can be *authors;* in the measure that someone fails to create a value, he feels prone to imitate, transmit, or serve as a representative of someone else's values, thus compensating for his lack of *authority* with an excess of *actority*.

The old-fashioned teachers, deprived of a knowledge of child psychology, needed to apply punishments continuously in order to secure external, apparent order in their schools. They were able in this manner to obtain but a small output from their pupils. Modern teachers, acquainted with the principles of educational psychology, make their pupils feel free in class and do not compel them to work under the threat of punishment; in spite of such an apparent relaxation of school discipline, such teachers are loved by their pupils and succeed in creating in them internal order, which will prevail all their lives even in the absence of the controller.

So enormous a change as that accomplished in dealing with pupils has been also applied in the domains of psychiatry and criminology in dealing with the insane and delinquent. Why should it not be applied in dealing with average, plain, normal adults? Modern army psychologists have advised the acceptance of such points of view to secure a new basis for army discipline and efficiency, and we shall discuss its effects among the Spanish Republican, German, and Soviet armies. Before we enter upon this matter it may be well to say a word about the technique that was used to encourage fellowship and mutual confidence among the combatants of the Spanish Republican Army, as well as to acquaint the men with the general principles of mental hygiene.

THE SPANISH REPUBLICAN BOOKLET
ON MENTAL HYGIENE

The booklet that we shall discuss was intended to be delivered to every literate man in our army. In each military unit it was to be discussed at several meetings; all men, no matter what their rank, were called upon by morale officers (*comisários políticos*), military physicians, and trained psychiatrists to say a word about it, and were also asked to add something of their own. We were not afraid when such discussions invaded the fields of philosophy, politics, religion, ethics, or sociology. I always maintained the view that every man, even if he is stupid, has some ideas concerning these matters and that all his behavior, in peace as in war, is referred to them. Hence, not to speak about such questions is as silly as not to speak about sexual problems when dealing with adolescents: they will find a way to discuss all these behind the backs of those whose duty it is to enlighten them.

Unfortunately, in spite of all efforts, such discussions could not be maintained in all sectors of the front. In those where they did take place, it was easy to observe the beneficial effects. Many original suggestions for improving the efficiency and well-being of the army were obtained; a higher morale was observed; and a noticeable decrease of abnormal mental reactions was registered.

Of course, I do not pretend that the text of the booklet I am about to quote could be universalized and directly applied to any other army. Each country must face its individual problems of mental hygiene; each nation has its own requirements for the peculiar psychological trends which justify a specific text to attain this aim. I feel, however, that in spite of such differences the general outline of my booklet would prove useful to inspire new ones. The booklet was composed of three different sections: in the first, the attention was called to the importance of mental hygiene; in the second, some of the most important problems of army life were discussed; in the third, the attempt was made to provide each man with a solid ethical basis for behavior, applicable not only to war but also to peace conditions, whatever his economic position, origin, and culture might be.

As previously mentioned, the booklet was first read by the men; then, in the special meeting, a group of twenty or thirty met with the mental hygienist or his representative to discuss it paragraph by paragraph. Any questions, remarks, objections, etc., were allowed, either openly or anonymously (written). The text of the booklet follows:

Miliciano: As soldier of the Popular Army ready to shed your blood and give your life for ideals and spiritual values; as comrade whose work and effort will form a better, more generous, and freer world: listen!

Pause a moment in the battle to hear in these few pages the well-intentioned voices of those who, unable to fight beside you with a gun, attempt to help you to victory with some advice stemming from their own scientific experiences and observations. Some of these are eternal maxims which can serve you not only today, but tomorrow and always as a guide for the attainment of your desires. For your own sake and that of all of us, do not forget them!

Of what use is a healthy body and all imaginable wealth if the owner, because of a weak, unhealthy, and deformed mind, cannot enjoy them and is incapable of using them for anything but the lowest animal desires? Of what use are dreams of beautiful horizons if the courage or will to conquer them does not exist? Only a healthy mind has sufficient strength to orient itself and fulfill its destiny in life. Spiritual health manifests itself directly by serenity and steadiness of purpose in face to the future, and by an attitude of loyalty, understanding, and warm affection toward one's fellowmen.

In exactly the same manner that we follow rules of physical hygiene to attain and to maintain bodily health, just so must we follow rules of mental hygiene to secure spiritual health.

The most simple machine, no matter how strong or well constructed, can be ruined if it is not correctly used and well treated. Similarly the human spirit can become exhausted if the rules of mental hygiene are not observed, for only these will preserve it from the disastrous effects of mental conflicts, dissatisfaction, and remorse. Grief, disappointment, resentment, or deeply repressed passion may affect an individual's life more severely than pneumonia or typhoid fever, even driving the victim to madness and suicide.

The *first rule* for the battle front is to isolate and to denounce those who, expressing either their natural pessimism or their ill will toward their country, spread depressing or disagreeable news and aid defeatist campaigns. Alarming news, whether true or false, spreads through the fighting front faster than any infection and may lead to a precipitous collapse of morale. Those who defy death are under much emotional tension. This increases suggestibility and facilitates belief in any cunning or false formula offering escape. "I must save my life to use it for the sake of my ideal," rationalizes the soldier, or he may try to persuade himself that "my individual sacrifice will be useless since I alone cannot avert defeat," etc. The mechanism underlying this mode of thought is the subconscious instinct of self-preservation which suggests "run away." To this the soldier's conscience replies: "I ought to remain at my post." Imagination, intermixed with fear, goes on to suggest: "The others are beginning to run," and finally conscience, overwhelmed, but seeking some justification for its surrender, states as the soldier flees: "It would be mad to stay and resist if my companions leave me." This latter statement is, of course, absolutely false, for despite others' flight, one's life is always better defended by facing the enemy than by presenting one's back to him: statistics show that deaths are five times greater in flight than in defense. Moreover, flight never serves as a useful sacrifice, not even having the golden value of an example. A thousand instances could be mentioned in which the visible sacrifice of one man has completely changed the course of a military action. That is why the defeatist *miliciano* is more dangerous than bullets. That is why he must not only be shunned as the plague, but also publicly denounced.

The second essential rule for the *miliciano's* mental hygiene is for him to feel strongly attached to his military group and to fulfill all the orders and assignments of his comrades in command. From the moment of his incorporation into an army corps, the *miliciano* must realize that individual initiative, disobedience, and lack of discipline lead to a dangerous decrease in the efficiency of the collective forces whose purpose it is to protect him. In addition they expose him to punishment and to the unpleasant effects of the loss of his dignity. A *miliciano* who disobeys or neglects an order is as bad as one who deserts from the fighting line. By alienating the support of his group, he may die like an amputated finger.

If you want to fulfill your responsibilities and obligations remember that you are fighting not only for a political regime or for social improvements, but for the future of all humanity. On your victory or defeat hinges a new world based on justice, liberty, and love, from which will arise a new joy in living for everyone in equal measure. You are therefore more than a giant—you are a creator, for from your hands will emerge part of the pattern of the new world. Be mindful of the importance of your effort. Concentrate on it and consciously devote to it all your energy. Do not fight to live! Live to fight!

In a short time, thanks to you and your comrades, predatory wars of invasion will be a thing of the past, and the citizens of the new world will seal a fraternal agreement, securing peace on earth forever for all men. For this it is necessary to direct all your courage to the battle. The more you long for a quiet and happy life, the more vigorously must you fight for early victory. Every hour that the war is prolonged causes new victims among your people. Save them with your will and energy in fighting. To do this you cannot squander your life in sexual excitement, all-night parties, or drink. *You must rest as much as you can during your leisure hours.*

If you feel exhausted, depressed, or doubtful; if you envy your comrades because they seem to suffer less or to weather the difficulties of the campaign better, remember that *a man's duty is not to compare himself with others, but with himself!* To become each day a more worthy person, to fight against your own selfish instincts, to overcome fear, to experience freedom, and to be better today than yesterday—this is your duty. In direct proportion to the accomplishment of this duty, you will feel happy even among the greatest calamities.

When you cannot control your emotions and passions, when your brain cannot solve your conflicts, when you feel incapable of recovering your self-control, go without hesitation to see your comrade, the physician, and explain your troubles to him. He will help you, treat you mentally and physically, and if he thinks it necessary will send you to a specialist. Have no shame in confessing your secret fears; reveal to him your innermost thoughts as you would a boil. Remember that his professional honor demands that he keep your confidence. Above all, do not seek the courage that you lack in drink or in excess of other poisons (coffee, tobacco, etc.). If you do so, you will accelerate your spiritual decline, rather than prevent it.

Now read and meditate on the following brief catechism. You will find enough in it to stimulate you to attain your highest goal—"nothing less than a complete man"—i. e., a reasonable, free, serene, fair, magnanimous, and productive human being.

Better to die on your feet than to live on your knees!

Your worst enemy is yourself. Observe and analyze yourself.

Never justify your own behavior on the basis of someone else's approval; always appeal to your own moral judgment as well.

Remember that those who shout most are usually most insecure.

Tell me of what you boast, and I will tell you what you lack.

The supreme good is justified satisfaction with oneself.

Do not judge the action of someone else until you know all his reasons.

A man's value is measured by the number of persons he understands and respects.

Do not entrust to others what you can do yourself.

Do not try to command if you have not learned to obey.

Words are silver; silence is gold.

Do not live in the past, but in the future, for man is what he becomes.

To triumph is good, but to forgive is better.

A good book is worth more than a bad companion.

Protect the weak, and honor all sincere opinions; oppose without mercy lies and hypocrisy, even though they seem to praise you.

Try to make each of your actions a model of universal behavior.

Follow the slogan: "One for all," rather than "All for one."

In addition to this booklet, which constituted the keystone of the mental hygiene work, different questionnaires were elaborated to be filled out by men suffering from any difficulties that necessitated their evacuation from the front line. It is well known that all war casualties have an infecting and demoralizing power, since they make those about them realize that they are exposed to the same fate. It is therefore important to keep all such casualties out of sight as far as possible, but it is desirable as well to devote particular care to their mental hygiene. One such questionnaire asked the subject for information as to (*a*) how he was affected by his present mishap; (*b*) what he did on the occasion; (*c*) what his present worries were; (*d*) what prospects he had for the near and remote future; (*e*) what he thought about the course of events; (*f*) what lessons he had drawn from his own experience and what warning he would like to give his comrades about war risks. Of course, all the answers were not expected to be sincere; they were merely used to reach the author and explore his mind without arousing in him the suspicion of being specially watched.

I also managed to have special boxes for complaints in hospitals, kitchens, headquarters, etc. These complaints were to be signed, and the subject was supposed to give his full identification, but a large percentage of the material collected in such boxes was either unsigned or written in an unintelligible form; finally this technique was discarded.

Special attention was to be devoted to those men guilty of military violations who had been transferred to special disciplinary battalions. The first task was to examine them psychiatrically, since most of them were either mentally retarded or psychopathic. The second task was to provide them with a better reaction pattern; the latter sometimes required a profound psychotherapeutic approach, in which the task of preventing further maladjustments combined with that of readapting them to their present situation.

GERMAN AND SOVIET POINTS OF VIEW

In spite of the radical differences in ideology and political structure between Germany and the U.S.S.R., both countries have effected very similar changes in their armies, compared with the organization they had during World War I. As my friend Professor Douglas Fryer points out in his forthcoming book on military psychology, both armies have introduced and combined the effects of military discipline with political stimulation of the soldiers. German officers, as well as Soviet officers, live far closer to the soldiers than the officers of the Allied armies usually do. Fryer quotes from reliable sources that "the Nazi soldiers gathered together each day for explanation by their officers of current political events so that each one might have immediate participation in them." The same is true of the Soviet soldiers. This contact is extended in both armies into other fields of activity, such as competitive games, entertainments, etc. The German and Soviet officers share the same risks and hardships as the men under their command; this is one of the peculiar trends of the so-called revolutionary armies, which should be introduced into the "traditional" armies as well in order to inject them with the "anti-apathetic serum." Most psychiatrists and officers of these old-fashioned armies complain of apathy and a lack of co-operation of many of their men: the latter are neither cowards nor rebels, but simply stand by and behave so as to avoid punishments, with the sole exception of a small group of enthusiasts and a small group of masochists, ex-hibitionists, or braggarts.

Apathy means passive resistance, and this is a form of resentment. In order to eliminate these attitudes there is no other method than to develop the confidence and faith of the men in their immediate superiors. These in their turn must trust and admire *their* superiors, because knowing them privately they have had occasion to feel that they are superior in *authority* and not merely in *actority*.

Such a concept requires the provision of great mobility in the commanding ranks; the immediate removal of those leaders who fail to win the affection and the admiration of their troops; and alteration of the classical rigidity of the military ranks.

A WORD ABOUT THE POSTWAR WORLD

A very intelligent friend of mine once said: "The explosion of the peace is more to be feared by the world than the end of the war." I think he was right, and I believe that the military psychiatrists will not end their duties as soon as the armistice is signed. On the con-trary, they will then be even more necessary than before. The sources of mental unrest and collective mental disorder are not to be found exclusively in the difficulty of the immediate life conditions. People become accustomed to the lack of food, the lack of enjoyment, and even the lack of personal security, provided they can see some future reward for their present sufferings. Everyone can cheat himself in a bad situation by continuously repeating: "Tomorrow it will be better." But if this "tomorrow" finally comes and it is not better, if it is the same or even worse than yesterday, because then there was at least a hope of happiness, then all the repressed feelings of disgust, hate, despair, and mistrust may lead to an abnormal outburst. Probably this is why almost all wars are followed by revolutionary periods, not limited to the losing side . . .

In the planning of the postwar world I have seen many projects emerging from politicians, sociologists, educators, and so on; yet I have not seen a single one coming from a congress of those men who are better equipped to understand the causes of individual and social imbalance and unrest: I refer to the psychiatrists. Of course the latter, alone, cannot bring about a solution that will promise a peaceful and happy life for mankind. They should, however, sit at all the tables where such an ambitious aim is attempted. Just because they are called upon to treat the worst, they deserve a word in eliminating the less serious causes of mental unrest, especially if they have schooled themselves in social psychiatry. Let us have faith in the future of this new branch of our science.

May the words pronounced by Samuel Hartwell, in his address to the American Orthopsychiatric Association in 1940, prove prophetic, so that we, psychiatrists, will in the near future be proud of helping to change this "valley of tears" into a "valley of peace and happiness," by devoting as much attention to the diseases of *collective persons* as we have hitherto directed to the diseases of individuals.

APPENDIX

MATERIALS

To perform the M.P.D., we require the following materials: (1) a wooden board, fifteen inches long and twelve inches wide; (2) a special test booklet containing the various forms of the test movements; (3) half a dozen drawing pins; (4) two sharp pencils; (5) an opaque sheet of paper, cardboard, or any other light material of rectangular shape, large enough to screen the subject's hand and the test sheet from his sight; (6) a metric ruler; (7) (eventually) a stop watch.

INSTRUCTIONS

The subject must be comfortably seated before a table or desk low enough to allow him to move his elbows freely in the air; its height must be about two or three inches above the subject's navel when seated. The distance between the subject's body and this table should be that customary for writing, but his position must not be at all oblique but exactly parallel to the longitudinal axis.

The first inner page of the text booklet will be attached to the center of the wooden board by drawing pins. The board should be centered on the table and placed in such a position that its midline concurs with the mesial or sagittal plane dividing the subject into left and right halves. Similarly, the horizontal lines drawn in the center of this page should parallel the longitudinal axis of the table and the anterior body surface of the subject.

Once these have been arranged, the subject is addressed as follows: "I am going to ask you to draw some lines in order to test the accuracy and regularity of your pulse. You must draw them without leaning your hand or your elbow anywhere, i. e., holding them in the air and letting them move freely. At the beginning you will draw the lines while you look at the model, but afterward a screen will be interposed and you will continue by heart, without seeing what you are doing. In spite of this, you will not stop drawing, but try to keep doing the same movement in the same place until I tell you to stop."

The M.P.D. consists of five serial tests: (1) basic lineograms or kinetograms; (2) zigzag lines; (3) staircase and circle; (4) chain; (5) parallel and U. The essential data can be obtained in the first parts of the test; the remainder are to be considered as a means of verifying, amplifying, or rectifying the preliminary data. Sometimes it is not necessary to complete the test booklet, but it is always indispensable to perform completely at least the first part. The test should be repeated after a certain interval, not less than twenty-four hours, and, if possible, not less than a week. The comparison between the results obtained in these two records will provide an index of the constancy or fidelity of the data. Of course this index will be much more accurate if the test is repeated several times and its results intercorrelated.

1. Obtaining the Lineograms

Once the subject is seated in the correct position, the examiner points out the right horizontal line in the first inside page of the booklet and says: "Hold the pencil with your right hand and kindly retrace this line again and again from one end to the other, performing an oscillating movement. Please do not stop or lift the pencil. Hold your wrist and your elbow in the air and try to keep within the line even when I screen you." When dealing with uneducated persons, the best the examiner can do is to illustrate his instructions by actions and to take the place of the subject, showing him what is required. In this lineogram, as in the remaining five of the page, the subject is allowed to perform three complete movements back and forth with visual control, and subsequently ten more screened.

After the right horizontal, the right sagittal, the left horizontal, and

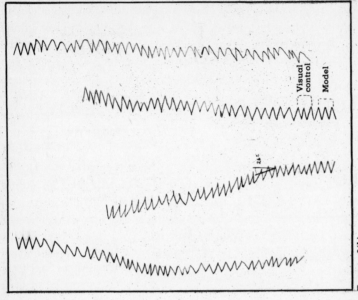

Figure 3(a).

Figure 3(b).

Visual control

Model

Vertical

Body

M.P.D. tracings of a selected (supernormal) adult.

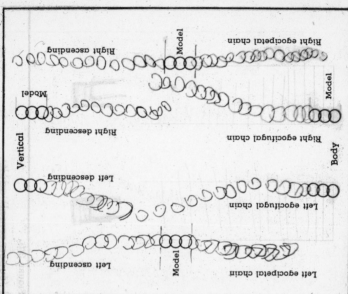

Right ascending

Model

Right egocentral chain

Vertical

Model

Right descending

Right egocifugal chain

Body

Left descending

Left egocifugal chain

Left ascending

Model

Left egocipetal chain

FIGURE 3(d).

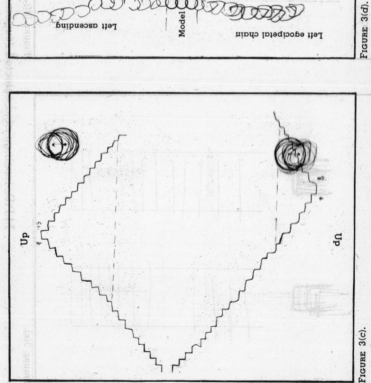

Up

Up

FIGURE 3(c).

M.P.D. tracings of a selected (supernormal) adult.

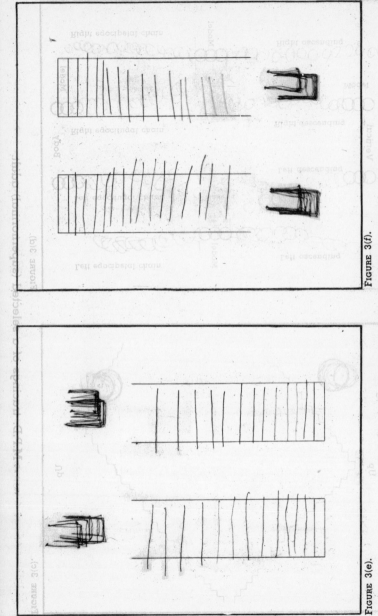

FIGURE 3(e).

FIGURE 3(f).

M.P.D. tracings of a selected (supernormal) adult.

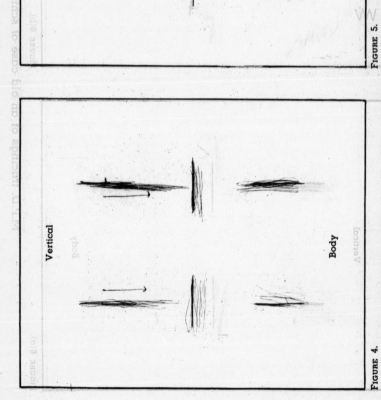

Vertical

Body

FIGURE 4.

M.P.D. tracings of an endogenous depression.

Vertical

Body

FIGURE 5.

M.P.D. tracings of a reactive depression.

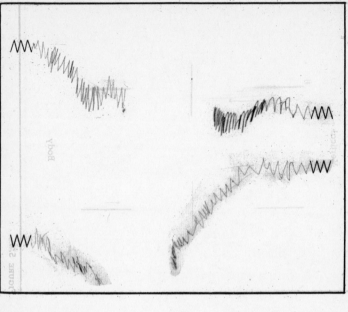

FIGURE 6(a).

FIGURE 6(b).

M.P.D. tracings of an old case of schizophrenia.

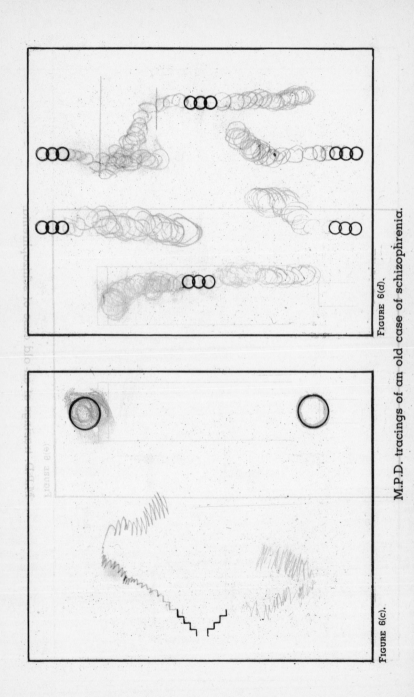

FIGURE 6(d).

FIGURE 6(c).

M.P.D. tracings of an old case of schizophrenia.

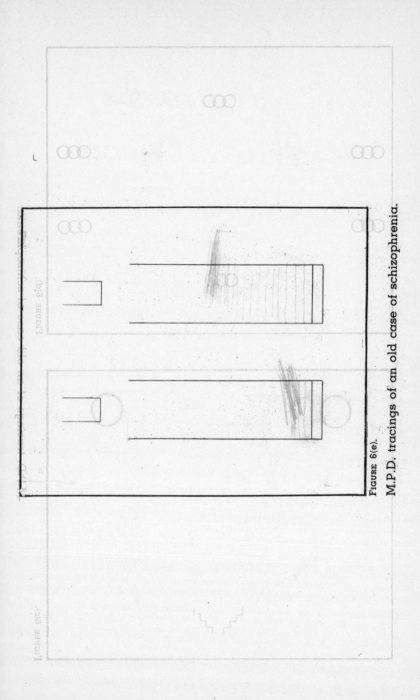

FIGURE 6(e).

M.P.D. tracings of an old case of schizophrenia.

the left sagittal lineograms are obtained. Then the wooden board is elevated to a vertical position and the subject is requested to perform right and left vertical lineograms with up and down movements. The same general directions and cautions are repeated, with the addition that the point of the pencil must be kept perpendicular to the model.

Since many people are curious to look at what they have already done, and this might discourage them or cause them to correct their shifts in the following drawings, the examiner must cover the drawings immediately after they are executed, using the same screen that has served to deprive the subject of visual control. When the examinee objects to this procedure, he is informed that he will see what he has done as soon as the whole test is concluded.

It is advisable that the examiner time each one of the requested series of movements, and also that he make a mark with a red pencil at each end of the first and last lines drawn by the subject without visual control.

2. OBTAINING THE ZIGZAG LINES

Once the leaf of the booklet has been turned and again fixed with the pins the examiner proceeds to obtain the outward zigzag, i. e., the one in which the subject's hands move from his body to the external world. The subject is now given a well-sharpened pencil in each hand, and is instructed as follows: "Will you please retrace these model lines, moving both pencils simultaneously and symmetrically inward and outward, just as if you were playing an accordion. When you have finished the models, please continue drawing the zigzag lines upon the white paper, trying to keep them of the same size and direction so as to make the design as regular and faithful to the model as possible. Do not stop or lift the pencil when I screen you, and remember that you must always hold your wrist and your elbow in the air and move your arms freely."

It is always advisable that the examiner lift the subject's elbows above the surface of the table, remarking that he is doing this in order to prevent the forearm from striking the edge at the end of the performance.

When one deals with absent-minded, confused, or dull persons, special attention must be devoted to avoid their attempting to draw a loop instead of an angle in the zigzag because of insufficient comprehension of the shape. This is a detail of great importance, since whenever the subject draws the loop in spite of understanding what he is asked to do, we must infer that he is suffering from an excess of tension of the flexor muscles of the arm. This is a sign of nervous or mental disturbance, especially frequent among schizophrenic patients; we call it the schizophrenic reversion and regard it as quite similar to schizophrenic negativism.

Another precaution to allay the fear of an individual that he may go off the paper when approaching the end of the sheet is to assure him: "Go on with your drawing until I tell you to stop, and do not worry, since I will warn you before you come to the end of the paper."

Some subjects begin the test with such coaction that they suspend the pencils over the paper without making a heavy enough mark. Then they must be cautioned to press more heavily, so that it will be easy to see their records afterward.

As usual, only three complete movements are allowed before screening. Differences in time of execution, especially between the first and second halves of the zigzag lines, are significant. As a matter of fact, in the anxiety states and in excited or elated patients there is a tendency to accelerate the movements and to increase the length of the lines, whereas in the states of inhibition, depression, and amazement a retardation of the movements, leading even to a complete cessation, may be observed. Whenever cessation occurs before expected, the examiner will make a special mark at that point and ask the subject to renew the movement until instructed to stop.

3. Obtaining the Staircase and Circle

Whereas the already described part of the test is designed to check the results of the sagittal lineograms, the one now to be described endeavors to check the results of the vertical lineograms. Sometimes a pause of five or ten minutes is advisable in order to avoid fatigue on the part of the subject.

To obtain the third part of the M.P.D., the corresponding sheet of the test booklet is fixed with the drawing pins in the wooden board. The latter is to be lifted and placed in the vertical position, in such a manner that the superior staircase, which is to be drawn by the right hand, is placed at the left of the subject and the circle comes to his right side.

The instructions are as follows: "Please follow the design of this staircase, retracing these steps with your pencil and continuing them up and to the right on the blank paper, without resting anywhere [sometimes the subject tries to do that by leaning his fingers on the paper] until I tell you to stop, and then you will begin to go down and to the right like this [the examiner should draw, it does not matter on what paper, the movement he expects]. Do not stop or rest during the test; try to make all the steps equal when going up and down. Remember that even when I interpose the screen you must keep making them by heart."

When the subject is about to reach the upper edge of the paper, bid him stop and descend, as already indicated. When he reaches the right edge, order him to cease.

Immediately after, show him the circle at the upper right and request him to retrace it continuously, keeping within it. When three turns have been completed, interpose the screen as always and obtain ten more turns. Once the test with the right hand is over, turn the leaf and proceed with the left hand, beginning with the staircase, which is placed at the right side and drawn up and to the left first, and then down and to the left. Analogically obtain the circular drawing with the left hand.

4. OBTAINING THE CHAINS

The next page of the test booklet contains six printed groups of three links each, which serve to form eight chains in the following manner: the two lower central are to be extended in an outer direction forming the egocifugal chains; the two lateral groups serve to begin the egocipetal chains and, when the board is in a vertical position, are the point of departure for the ascending ones; the two upper central groups are the beginning of the descending ones. To obtain them, adhere to the following order: (*a*) egocifugal and egocipetal chains of the right hand; (*b*) the same of the left hand; (*c*) ascending and descending chains of the right hand; (*d*) the same of the left hand.

The instructions the subject receives are: "Please retrace with your pencil, one by one, the links of this chain and extend it in the same direction, endeavoring to make all of the links the same size. You must not lean against anything to draw them, and remember to lift your pencil every time one is completed. Try not to twist the direction, and keep making the links until I tell you to stop, without ceasing when I interpose the screen."

The sagittal chains will be drawn with the forearm in the same position as used for the zigzag, i. e., with the elbow in the same plane as the hand, some centimeters above the surface of the table. The verticals will also be drawn with the elbows above the plane of inclination of the board and the subject will be warned not to be afraid of going off the paper (because if he fears this, he may diminish the amplitude of the ascending movements and give a false impression of depression when the graph is judged).

5. Obtaining the Parallels (Ladders) and *U*'s

The last two pages of the test booklet deal with the parallels and *U*'s. One begins with the left page, on which are printed two pairs of parallel lines. The subject is to divide these throughout their extent by means of transverse horizontal lines, so that each segment thus formed is equal to the one printed at the bottom. In other words, he is to draw evenly spaced rungs on a ladder, the sides and lowest rungs of which are already printed. Above are two *U*'s. The test is begun with the right hand and the subject is instructed: "Divide this space into parts similar to this [the examiner points with his finger or a pencil]. Draw the lines parallel to the model, and try to keep within the margins. You will begin from left to right and continue blindly until I tell you to stop." During the drawing of the first three parallel lines he is allowed visual control, but then the screen is interposed until he reaches the end or is about to go off the side of the paper. Immediately afterward, homologous drawings are obtained with the left hand, moving from right to left. Finally the board is lifted and the subject is requested to retrace the U in the same way as he previously did the circle.

After this page has been completed, one proceeds to the next with the same exercise but in an egocipetal sense, i. e., beginning to divide the distance from the end farther from the body and approaching it progressively. Ultimately, retrace the U placed in the lower portion of this page. Always allow three complete movements under visual control and then obtain ten more blind.

Data to Be Considered in the M.P.D.

Data to be considered are of two kinds: intrinsic or graphic (registered in the test) and extrinsic or verbomotor (gestures, attitudes, and remarks during or after the drawing). Later, chronological data are also to be considered: i. e., the time of execution of the different stages of the test; these, generally, are related to the psychic time of the individual, since no previous rate is fixed for the performance of his movements and he is free, within certain broad limits, to perform them slowly or rapidly.

For the sake of conciseness we shall deal only with the most important, that is to say, the graphic data. These consist of all the drawings made by the subject and are in turn subdivisible into quantitative and qualitative data. Since the M.P.D. must be performed at least twice, all data may be considered from the point of view of their interrelations (constancy, fidelity, periodicity, etc.), but since we wish to simplify as much as possible and to make this examination practical, we shall refer only to the data from the isolated examination of a single protocol. Let us begin with the quantitative data corresponding to each of the five divisions described above:

Lineograms

1) *Length.*—The length of the six models is four centimeters each. It is interesting to note whether the first line drawn *without* visual control is more or less than four centimeters; it is also desirable to measure the line last drawn so as to know what the natural tendency of the subject is, to increase, to decrease, or to maintain the initial length. The average length of lines corresponding to each hand, and the greater or lesser constancy of this length, expressed in terms of the mean quadratic deviation, is a very important factor as well.

2) *Direct lineal shifting.*—This is the most expressive of the measures. We must take into account its direction and degree. There is a natural tendency in the normal subject to deviate in every oscillating movement in the direction in which the movement has been initiated. However, the amount of this deviation is practically negligible and it hardly attains more than a few millimeters in our test. Its production can be explained by the motor autoinduction phenomenon which is to be observed in the excess of the initial movement over the return. However, to eliminate the possibility of its increase in some suggestible subjects it is advisable when verifying the test control to request these persons to begin the movement in the direction opposite to the one they began the first time.

Each pair of kinetograms belongs to a different plane of motion, and its deviations likewise acquire various significances, as we shall see later. We are now concerned in emphasizing that the sense of the deviation is given by the relative position of the final line in relation to the model, and its degree is expressed by the distance between the middle points of each.

Although, as a rule, after the lineal deviation has been initiated in one direction it persists and increases in proportion to the number of movements performed in the series, in some cases it undergoes a spontaneous reversal in the course of execution, so that the amount of the deviation at the third and fourth movements, for instance, is greater than at the end. This occurs especially in unstable and doubtful persons who lack orientation and are devoid of a definite characterological structure. When this occurs more than once during the drawings it is well to study it apart by asking the subject to draw, instead of the same line in two directions, parallel lines, very close together, in an alternately opposite direction. This will enable us to measure all the elemental deviations (absolute) together with the final deviation (relative).

3) *Axial deviation.*— In this case we are dealing not only with a total displacement of the lines, which go off by one or both ends, but with a twisting of the axis of movement itself, so that the lines oscillate about an imaginary center, i. e., the drawing loses its parallelism in relation to the model. This deviation can be observed either in one of the excursions of the oscillation, being compensated by the other, or in both. Its pathological significance is undoubtedly greater in the latter case. It can be measured by the angle formed by the most deviated or twisted line and the model. If it takes place in only one of the oscillating movements, but the final lines are correct, it may be imputed to momentary lack of constraint or to a change in the kinetic attitude of the subject. This deviation is more frequently observed in the horizontal and sagittal kinetograms than in the verticals.

4) *Secondary lineal deviation.*—This is produced, not in the sense of the movement, but in a plane perpendicular to it. Thus, in the right horizontal kinetogram, the direct lineal deviation is produced toward the right, toward the left, or in both directions, while the secondary lineal deviation will be up (outward), down (inward), or up and down. This secondary lineal deviation in normal and equilibrated persons is greater than the direct deviation and can be explained by the effort of the subject to keep within the ends of the line he is drawing, which causes him to neglect the precaution of changing the direction at the very moment he begins the return movement, so that the action of the subject's predominant tension in the perpendicular plane emerges. Accordingly, this secondary deviation is gener-

ally found related to the direct deviation of the perpendicular kine-togram; in this manner, when the subject deviates secondarily toward the top (outward) and directly toward the right in the drawings of the right-hand kinetogram, we can be almost sure that he will deviate secondarily toward the right (outward) and directly toward the top in the drawing of the sagittal kinetogram of this hand. We can even state that the tendency restrained through the execution of one phase of an oscillation appears manifest during the execution of the other, and *vice versa,* producing a kind of correspondence between the direct and secondary deviations of the various kinetograms, which will be clearer as the force of the existing tendencies increases. The intensity of this secondary deviation is to be measured by the width of the sheaf of lines drawn in each experiment.

Zigzags

1) *The dominant hand.*—As this test is to be performed simultaneously with both hands, the kinetic impulse is rarely distributed symmetrically and equally. Generally the subject's attention is attracted by the right hand and the left follows it like its shadow. Sometimes, on the contrary, the left hand is the one that monopolizes the whole attention and the right is constrained to accompany it. At other times they alternate as to dominance. When we deal with mental patients, a fourth possibility exists: each hand may act in its own way, quite independent of its mate, thus producing two absolutely different zigzags. The dominant hand is the one that moves more rapidly and produces a steadier, more rhythmic drawing.

2) *Relation between the extent of the egocifugal and egocipetal movements.*—In order to establish this relation we measure with a rule a distance of approximately ten centimeters beginning with the fifth zigzag made in each direction without visual control, count the number of angles contained in this distance, and divide the number of egocifugal by the number of egocipetal angles. The more acute the egocifugal angles are, the larger the numerator and, hence, the quotient. We can also say that when the extensor movement of the arm

is more difficult than that of flexion, the quotient increases, and *vice versa.*

3) *Zero and inverted angles.*—The predominance of the flexor attitude over the extensor during the sagittal advancement may be so great that upon arriving at the end of the line and losing the initial impulse, the new movement lacks extending impulse and is made upon the previous line or even loses ground and gives place to a loop. This phenomenon is called praxical reversion and gives rise to the presence of zero or inverted angles in the egocifugal zigzag. It may also occur in the egocipetal zigzag if the extensor movement greatly predominates over the flexor, i. e., if the subject has a subconscious resistance against drawing against himself (ego vulnerability). In asthenic, debilitated, and fatigable persons, some of these reversions or abrogations of the egocifugal advancement may be observed at the end of the zigzag, even if the advancement has been normal up to this time: the pathologic impressiveness of this datum is the greater the earlier it appears in the drawing and the more frequently it occurs. If it reaches a certain limit, it invariably appears together with the axial deviation of the zigzag that we are to study next.

4) *Axial deviation.*—The direction of the zigzag should be perpendicular to the plane of the subject. Nevertheless, this situation seldom prevails, and it is common to observe a deviation or a twist in the drawing more marked in the egocifugal than in the egocipetal zigzag. This deviation may be uni- or bilateral, open or closed, sinuous, etc. When an attitude of introversion predominates in the subject, the zigzags tend to approach each other, and we can even observe an interlacing of the pencils that leads to a cessation of the drawing unless one of the hands is sufficiently ahead of the other that the pencils never come into contact. On the contrary, when there is a tendency to abduction (increase of the "vital space") the zigzags open in the egocifugal movements, as if they were to embrace the world with their arms. In the egocipetal movement, concurring with the appearance of some reversion, an axial deviation of the zigzag with a tendency to go off the paper can also be observed in one or both hands,

as if the subject subconsciously were trying to elude the contact of the pencils with his own body.

5) *Loss of the praxical configuration.*—The significance of this is purely pathological. It consists of the disorganization of the twofold zigzag movement, which is then replaced by a veritable tumult of elemental movements of various sizes and directions in one or both hands. The more manifest examples belong to lesions of the neuraxis and to progressive psychoses, as we shall very soon see.

Staircase and Circle Data

As we already know, these tests are executed in a vertical plane and are chiefly designed to verify the results of the vertical kinetograms. Essential data include:

1) *Relationship between the number of ascending and descending steps.*—In order to obtain this we draw a horizontal line from the third step traced without visual control to cut the descending drawing on the other side. We then count the number of steps up and down and divide the number of ascending by the number of descending steps. If going up has been more difficult than going down, the height of the steps will be less and the horizontal lines will dip down, producing a loss of height, so that there will be more steps and the quotient will exceed unity—vice versa, if the ascending movements are easily performed and the descent has to overcome a tendency to lift the arm, the quotient will be fractional.

2) *Relative extent of the drawing in its two phases.*—Generally speaking, this is related to the greater or lesser difficulty in its execution; the easier the movement of ascent or descent is, the more it tends to overpower the horizontal drawing, and therefore the extent of the staircase is narrower; on the contrary, when there is some difficulty in the way up or down, the length of the horizontals is increased, because the latter serve as a relative rest to the subject in his work.

3) *Reversions.*—It is frequent to observe an inversion or reversion in the drawing of one or more steps when dealing with patients who have little understanding or who suffer from severe psychotic dis-

orders. Sometimes although this reversion is not produced, we observe an alteration of the shape from steps to teeth. Finally, stupid persons tend to sharpen the right angles, so that the result of the performance is more like a vertical zigzag than a staircase.

4) *Disorganization of the praxical configuration.*—The loss of the integrity of movement, which results in the replacement of the staircase by a series of pothooks more or less imbricated and unexpressive, is distinctly pathologic.

5) *Displacements and alterations of the size of the circles.*—The size of the circles drawn upon the model varies in relation with the size of the lineal kinetograms. The same alterations occur in their displacement as of the vertical kinetograms. Whenever there is a decrease in the psychomotor tension (kinetic energy) we observe a fall in the circles. When there is an increase, due to excitement, we observe a rise. Both movements are usually associated in a secondary displacement, toward the left or right; the same occurs in the kinetograms. As a rule, movements of the circle downward and inward are associated, as are also upward and outward movements. As we shall see later, in the anxiety states a continuous increase of the circular diameter is noted, which is produced by the easy irradiation of the scheme of movement.

Data Obtainable from the Chains

The chains are an alternative test to check the data already obtained with the lineograms, the zigzags, and the staircase. It is through the drawing of the chains that we can better appreciate the qualitative variations that form individual style. Nevertheless, we shall now refer merely to the quantitative alterations which are to be noted as follows:

1) *Relationship between the initial and the final sizes of the links.*—This datum must be related with the corresponding data in the respective kinetograms.

2) *A tendency to break or, vice versa, to heap the chain.*—The first arises when the flow of the advancing movement in the drawing results in the links becoming untied, i. e., they are not imbricated like

the model. The second occurs when, as a consequence of the antago-
nistic movement, there is want of impulse to proceed in the already
begun direction and the subject repeats the drawing in the same place,
or even hesitates and instead of drawing a chain, finishes by drawing a coil.

3) *Degree of closure of the links.*—If the subject finishes each link
before or after arriving at the point of departure, it will be open or
superclosed. The first case we should impute to negligence; the second, to excessive precaution or to perseveration in the execution of
each elemental movement.

4) *Dextrogyrate or levogyrate circles.*—The links may be drawn
clockwise or counterclockwise. It is advisable to take note of this
datum, since it is always derived from detrogyrate or levogyrate predominance.

5) *Degree of accuracy of the chain.*—The accuracy of the sagittal
chains is usually homologous to that of the zigzag. In the vertical
chains, it is altered according to the difficulty of the drawing: the
heaping and the twisting concur. As in this test the maintenance of
the direction is disturbed by the continuous interruptions of the drawing, it is almost exceptional to perform it without a slight deviation.
This is the most discontinuous part of the M.P.D.

Data of the Parallels and *U*'s

The object of the parallel test is to verify and to supplement the
data already obtained in the sagittal drawings (kinetograms, zigzags, and chains). It is a matter of the greatest interest to determine
whether the advancing movement, outward and inward, is of a regular uniform type or not and whether it is fluent or suffers any noticeable alteration in its course, since our experience shows us that any
alteration of the relationship between the ego and the world, which
is indispensable for the sake of psychic counterbalance, reveals itself
more clearly in the sagittal plane than in any other. In fact, more or
less abnormal drawings in the horizontal and vertical planes are
still consistent with normality in overt behavior, but the latter is al-

ways disordered when perceptible modifications are observed in the sagittal plane. The data we endeavor to obtain in this stage of the M.P.D. are as follows:

1) *The relationship between the amplitude of the standard distance and the average of the parallels drawn by the subject with each hand and in each direction.*—The width of each segment of the model is about eight millimeters and forms the numerator of a fraction whose denominator is the arithmetical mean of each of the four tests performed by the subject. Consequently, we obtain four quotients, those belonging to the egocifugal and egocipetal movements of each hand. These will be greater or less than unity, depending on whether the average distance between lines drawn by the subject falls short of or exceeds the standard.

2) *Difference between the three maximum and minimum distances of each series.*—Calculate the average of the three widest segments and that of the three narrowest ones. If the segments are negative, the subject has inverted the sense of the movement. If the difference between the widest and the narrowest segments exceeds the amplitude of the standard, we must infer a disorder.

3) *Maximum angular value of the lineal torsion in relation to the standard parallels.*—This value is to be measured with a goniometer in each series.

4) *Deviation of the drawing in relation to the marginal or greater parallels (sides of the ladder).*—This is a consequence of the axial deviation of the zigzag and under normal conditions is related to the corresponding deviation no matter in what direction. If the deviation is of an intense degree, in the course of the movement the hand moves back obliquely and the line it draws cuts the preceding one, forming an *x,* a cross, or the wing of a windmill. If this occurs with a certain frequency, we are sure to observe reversions in the zigzag. The converse, however, is not true, since reversion in the zigzag may be a consequence of negligence in the maintenance of its shape on the part of the subject if his attention is poor. That is why we attribute greater pathological significance to the existence of crossing in the parallels

than to reversions in the zigzag; the concurrence of both is, of course, most significant.

5) *Mean value of the lineal amplitude and dominant tendency in its variation.*—The relationship existing between the average length of the horizontal lines drawn by the subject and the average of the standard lines should be compared with the corresponding ratio in the horizontal kinetograms. The fact that the lines in the parallel test are not superposed as they were previously allows us to appreciate whether a definite tendency to increase or to decrease lineal size exists; such a tendency may be independent of the tendency to increase or to decrease the sagittal advancement. Likewise we shall observe whether there are fluctuations in this tendency: these characterize the unstable personality.

The *U*'s represent the last control of the data already obtained in the vertical and sagittal planes. In this test, the basic movements of ascent and descent, extension and flexion are separated by a neutral interval, expressed by the interposed horizontal line that interrupts the biphasic oscillations. With the help of this device we can elude the motor suggestibility or the kinetic automatism that leads to the perseveration and exaggeration of the initial shifts by virtue of a reciprocal induction phenomenon. On the other hand, the kinetic pattern becomes confused so that slight disorders that might be overshadowed in the preceding tests are revealed. The data to be observed here are as follows: the initial and final size of the *U*'s, the direct and secondary deviation, the straightness or axial torsion, and, above all, the correspondence between the results here and those obtained in the previous stages of the M.P.D.

NORMAL AND PATHOLOGICAL FINDINGS

We have worked with the following groups of patients: (*a*) presumably normal adults of both sexes (87 males and 63 females); (*b*) selected adults chosen on the basis of their proved counterbalance and harmonious character (18 males and 11 females); (*c*) normal or slightly psychotic children, from 7 to 13 years of age (25 males and 6 females); (*d*) young people and adults, mentally abnormal at the time of the examination (482 males and 456 females).

The accurate statistical elaboration of these results is not yet concluded and, moreover, in nearly 20 per cent of the cases the examination has not as yet been repeated or has been repeated with some technical variation which prevents us from using the results with complete certainty. Because of these limitations, our statements are provisional, although we doubt that they will be essentially modified by more completely elaborated statistics. It is necessary to add that some of the concrete data have been investigated among special social groups (delinquents, etc.) by some contributors, but we do not intend to refer to them in this chapter, devoted exclusively to that part of the M.P.D. which concerns the neuropsychiatrist.

Group of Normal Adults

The general results indicate:

1) A decrease in the lineal size of the first lineogram drawn without visual control in the horizontal and sagittal right kinetograms is normal (average length 3.6 centimeters as against 4 centimeters of the model). This decrease is still greater in the female groups (3.5 centimeters).

2) There exists a slight tendency to increase the lineal size throughout the execution of the drawings so that, for instance, the average size of the final lineogram of the right horizontal is about 4.4 centimeters. This tendency to increase the lineal amplitude is more clearly observed in the vertical kinetograms, although in these it is chiefly expressed by the elongation of the descending movement in the final lines, probably representing the beginning of muscular fatigue.

3) The left-hand lineograms are longer than those of the right hand in every plane; in the horizontal, the values of the initial and final lineograms are, respectively, 4.3 and 5 centimeters.

4) The direct lineal deviations, contrary to what might be expected, are not perceptibly greater in the left kinetogram. On the

whole, the average is about six millimeters in the right hand and eight millimeters in the left. Their direction varies greatly from one subject to another and even changes at times in the same individual. It may be stated, however, that they usually occur in the sense of the initial movement of the horizontal lineogram, during the egocifugal movement in the sagittal, and in the descent in the right vertical. If we designate with positive signs those belonging to movements of abduction, extension, and elevation of the arm, and with negative signs the opposite, the algebraic sum of the averages in this group is practically zero, but still has a positive sign (0.1 centimeter). Eighty-five per cent of our normal individuals have exhibited lineal deviations in some direction, varying between one and two centimeters. Only 2 per cent have manifested isolated deviations greater than two centimeters. In no case has the total average of the deviations exceeded 1.5 centimeters, and the average total of deviation of the group is less than a centimeter.

5) The axial deviation is insignificant in the lineograms. It is only observable in the left horizontal and sagittal of 7 cases out of 150, and has an average angular value of 7 degrees.

6) The secondary lineal deviation is perceptibly greater in the left hand than in the right, but we have not yet calculated the averages. In any case, they are inferior to those of the pathologic groups.

7) The analogy between the direct lineal deviations in the lineograms with the corresponding algebraic signs, according to the already designated criterion (4) expresses what might be called the degree of symmetry between the pulsations predominant in both cerebral hemispheres. The less this analogy, the greater the derangement in the praxia, and the more difficult the fluidity of the individual behavior. Hence I call this value the *coefficient of coherence*. As would be expected, it is greater in the groups of normal adults than in the various psychopathic groups and less in the former than in the chosen adults (c.c. averages 0.74, 0.53, 0.85 respectively, in twenty cases of each group).

8) The analogy between the direct lineal deviations of one hand

in two identical tests with an interval between, on the page containing the lineograms, is the basis for the *constancy or fidelity* of the traits revealed by the test. In 1939 we observed with great amazement that it is greater for the left kinetograms than for the right, which practically means that, with the exception of left-handed persons, the right hand is more unsteady in its results and portrays in a better way the momentary variations of the subject's attitude, while the left is less likely to be influenced by them and maintains its deviations in a more permanent way. Thus, in twenty cases the mean value of this analogy was 0.73 for the right kinetograms and 0.88 for the left.

Group of Selected Adults

In view of the frequency of the psychopathic personality, it is evident that the random selection of the "man on the street" to establish norms of psychic equilibrium must be somewhat risky. Accordingly, on beginning the investigation, Professor Aubrey Lewis and I decided to create a small control group of persons about whom, judging from history and conduct, there was no suspicion of characterological anomalies or strong genotypic imperfections. The results obtained in London with this group convinced me of the excellence of the M.P.D. We obtained with it clear drawings and such consistent results that we were supported in our belief that in the previous group there were some undiagnosed psychopaths; at the same time, the test gave us the means to differentiate them. In the course of the two years that I have been living in Argentina I have changed the original technique sufficiently to require a new verification, and I have endeavored to assemble another control group; in all, I have obtained kinetograms from eighteen males and eleven females who would be considered supernormal, not as to intelligence, but as to calmness, balance, and harmony of behavior. Here are, briefly summarized, their main differences from the group of adults taken at random: (*a*) a smaller difference between the length of the models and the drawings; (*b*) a smaller average of direct and secondary lineal deviations; (*c*) a complete absence of axial deviations; (*d*) larger coefficients of coherence and constancy. To save space, since they are not essential to our purpose, we omit the exact statistical data.

Group of Children

This is the weakest part of our work, because we do not yet possess sufficient material on which to base any conclusions, even of a provisional nature. Nevertheless, the simple general inspection of the drawings obtained in the thirty-one cases we have examined serves to indicate that a *great many of the alterations that will be depicted in the groups of pathological adults are found, even in an exaggerated form, in the juvenile drawings.* This fact confirms from another point of view what could have been expected beforehand: the right hand is more related to the present personality and the left hand better indicates the constitutional trends. As a consequence of the slight development of personality in children, both hands express almost identical data, while in cultivated adults the left hand reveals the genotypic and primary phenotypic contribution, sometimes in contradistinction to the secondary paratypic contribution; in short, the left hand is *temperamental* and the right is *characterological.* The lack of integration in the complex configurations is singularly characteristic of the juvenile drawings, as well as the axial deviation in the *sagittal plane:* this is caused by the impossibility which the subject, deprived of visual control, experiences of compensating for the instinctive tendency to move the hand, the pencil, and the elbow in the same oblique axis corresponding to the plane of semiflexion in which these parts are placed in relation to the arm. By this same fact is explained the juvenile tendency to twist the head in writing and to twist the paper analogously so as to place it in a position perpendicular to this axis. This compensatory function of secondary importance is the one to be lost as soon as the co-ordinates of the rational space-time become disorganized.

The similarity between some juvenile kinetograms and those of pathological adults is such that, in the absence of any other data, it may be difficult to distinguish between them; nevertheless, the former are generally characterized by the imprecision and dysrhythmia of the elementary movements, whereas in the latter, a disturbance in the co-ordination of these movements predominates. In other words, children tend to manifest alterations in the intrakinetic impulses which overshadow the interkinetic anomalies.

Youths and Adults with Mental Abnormalities

This group, without doubt the most abundant in our material since it comprises 938 cases, may be broken down into several subgroups, according to the predominant psychopathology. It is to be noted that the M.P.D. offers sufficient data to enable us to deduce this psychopathology in correlation with the clinical manifestations and the personal histories, as we shall see. However, as in the present case we are concerned with a test of attitudes of reaction, in which the verbal expressions may serve to express or to dissimulate, the control of the results will be established not so much by the language functions as by the acts the subjects perform spontaneously. Let us begin by summarizing the results which the M.P.D. has afforded in the most common psychosis—schizophrenia.

1. Patients Suffering from the Schizophrenic Syndromes: Among the clinical material we may distinguish the following types: (1) reactive forms; (2) initial accesses of schizophrenic processes; (3) temporarily inactive processes (either spontaneously or as the result of insulin treatment); (4) terminal forms with irreversible deterioration of personality (Kraepelin's *Verbloedung*).

Before citing the differential characteristics of the M.P.D. we must say that the abnormal elements found in the cases in which the clinical diagnosis of a schizophrenic syndrome was unquestionable have been the following: (*a*) disorientation or axial twisting, preferably visible in the sagittal kinetograms; (*b*) a tendency to reverse the movement being performed; (*c*) a tendency to the disintegration of the configurations; (*d*) irregularity of the impulse, sometimes notable in the weakening of the impulse and at other times in sudden increases of speed, intensity, and extent; (*e*) lack of synchronization of the combined simultaneous movements of both hands in the zigzags.

To these signs we may add a peculiar general qualitative impression in all the drawings of clumsiness, crudity, and lack of style. There is a pluriformity explainable by the lack of integration in the personal synthesis of its author. Let us see how these signs are combined in the above mentioned clinical forms.

1) *Reactive forms of the schizophrenic syndromes.*—We use this name to designate those reactions in which the symptomatology, no matter how elaborate it may be, is psychologically comprehensible and is motivated or produced by psychological conflicts and situations capable of altering the individual's mode of reaction without compromising seriously the fundamental architecture of the personality, so that the case is capable of complete recovery. These forms are expressed in the M.P.D. by the predominance of the alterations in the hand more easily controlled by the subject in his everyday tasks: the right in the right-handed, the left in the left-handed; by the satisfactory maintenance of the configurations or kinetic patterns of a complex type (staircases, chains, U's); and by the slight degree of axial disorientation in comparison with the high degree of the signs of introversion and active negativism: great interiorization of the horizontal kinetograms and numerous reversions at the end of the zigzag.

2) *Acute active processes.*—In these we find almost constantly the so-called paranoid focus, distinguished by the peculiar confluence of the direct deviations of the right kinetograms toward the center of the paper. The existence of reversions and axial torsion of the zigzags, the crossing of the parallels, and the deviation of the U's can likewise be appreciated, chiefly in the egocifugal drawings. Yet the complex configurations are fairly well maintained; there is no loss in the style or general architecture of the kinetic patterns initiated under visual control. In proportion to the advancement of the process and to the disintegration of the deeper levels of the personality, i. e., in proportion to the establishment of rigidity, obstruction, and schizophrenization of the individual—as a consequence of the dis-

junction and the blocking of the psychoneuric sources—the symptoms in both hands proceed to level and, above all, the global forms of the kinetic drawings become affected: the chains are distorted, dislocated, and clouded; the staircase is transformed into an incoherent conglomerate of movements; and the zigzag disappears, giving place to a band, thick in some parts and thin in others, but always hazy because of the intercrossing of lines in various directions. When we witness all these disorders in both hands, we may be sure that previous accesses have occurred or that we are dealing with a form of *schizocaria* (Mauz's *catastrophic schizophrenia*) in which the virulence of the process leads to a rapid collapse of personality. If there are no genotypic antecedents we must seek the cause in some organic factor (infection, toxin, endocrine disorder, etc.) complicating the disease.

3) *Temporarily inactive processes.*—When, either spontaneously or as the result of treatment, the process becomes inactive, we observe not only the satisfactory reintegration of personality by virtue of the compensatory functions, but also a change in the M.P.D. with the almost complete disappearance of the alterations in the right-hand drawings, although the abnormal traits still persist in those of the left hand. In case the subject is left-handed, these phenomena have no diagnostic value, but we do not possess enough material to state that the phenomena are inverted. The persistence of the process after an apparent remission is especially revealed by the indistinctness and inexactness of the left staircase, the chain, and the zigzag, as well as by the interlacing of the parallels of the same side.

4) *Terminal forms.*—Here one observes the entire gamut of changes in *both hands*. The great secondary deviation in the horizontal drawings is to be especially noted (inexactness of the kinetogram in the more easily controlled direction), as well as the dissolution of the kinetic configurations or patterns, and as a result the lineograms are transformed into veritable pencil spots.

By means of modern treatments, such as Sakel's treatment, Meduna's treatment, electric shocks, etc., for schizophrenic attacks, we are able to condense the development of the psychosis into a short period and we are supplied with an excellent opportunity to study the parallels between the clinical recovery and the improvement of the kinetograms. The M.P.D. furnishes a reliable criterion to predict the recurrence of the disease as long as we adhere to these criteria: when the right-hand alterations disappear and those of the left hand continue the same or become worse, we may expect an incomplete recovery, with the danger of recurrence at any moment. The integrity of the left hand—that is, the disappearance of the reversions in the sagittals—indicates whether to stop or to continue treatment, once apparent improvement of the symptoms has been obtained.

2. Patients Suffering from Cyclophrenic Syndromes: The decrease in the frequency with which this diagnosis has been made during the past twenty years is surprising. In Spanish statistics of seventeen thousand mental patients, compiled in 1933, 9.25 per cent of the cases were still so classified; although at the present time one can hardly find two such cases out of a hundred. The cause of this decrease is that as soon as schizophrenic symptoms appear in the course of a psychosis, the prevailing tendency is to diagnose schizophrenia without taking into account the rare occurrence of mental illness without some such manifestations. However, an evaluation of the symptoms according to their importance should be made before a definite diagnosis is concluded as to the essential nature of the clinical process.

While working at the Maudsley Hospital in London with a very small number of patients in whom the diagnosis of a manic-depressive syndrome was confirmed beyond doubt by individual and genotypic antecedents, I had the opportunity to assure myself that the more characteristic kinetogram alterations occurred in the vertical plane. The variations corresponded in magnitude to the intensity of the basic symptom on the diathetic scale of Kretschmer which ranges from elation to depression. In a manner analogous to the "vital feelings" of Schneider, we observed changes in the psychomotor tension that led to a facilitation of the ascending and descending movements in the vertical plane and impressed typical variations in the drawings of the M.P.D.

According to the results of the M.P.D. we may distinguish various clinical types in the cyclophrenias. The subtypes include: (1) simple asthenic depressions; (2) dysthymic depressions; (3) false anxiety depressions; (4) psychogenic depressions (reactive or focal).

1) *Asthenic depressions.*—In these we observe a decrease in the vertical kinetograms, precipitancy of the descending staircase, a heaping of the ascending chains, the breaking of the descending ones, and fall of the circle. There is no increase of aggressiveness (sagittal advancement), introversion of the lineograms, or appreciable alteration of the length of the latter.

2) *Dysthymic depressions.*—The phenomena engendered in these are more the result of the *rage experienced by the subject against himself* than the result of the complete absence of reactive forces or energies. As a consequence, although it is true that the depressive symptoms above depicted persist, they are accompanied by a frank inversion of the horizontal kinetograms, an increase and irregularity of their length, and a facilitation of the egocipetal movement in the zigzags and parallels.

3) *False anxiety depressions.*—These correspond to the previously designated agitated depressions and are really syndromes of an almost toxic nature, in which, together with an acceleration of the psychic time and an uninhibitable need for movement signs of uncontrolled emotional ambivalence prevail: the subject oscillates between fear and despair without feeling sad or depressed, but only hemmed in and misplaced. The characteristics of his myokinetic phenomena are the acceleration of all movements and the continual increase of their length throughout all the tests. This is how we may observe the so-called heating which is the translation of a predominance of the processes of irradiation over those of concentration in the cerebral surface. In these cases we are surprised by the maintenance of the axial directions and by the complex myokinetic configurations, and

yet some enormous secondary deviations may be observed in the drawings of oligophrenics, in which there is also a complete absence of restraint on the part of the cerebral surface; but the difference between them can be established not only by the greater accuracy and precision of the elementary drawings but also by the maintenance of the configurations, in spite of the great rapidity of the drawing. Moreover, in these psychoses the temperamental basis is evinced by means of the peculiarities of the direct deviations of the kinetograms.

4) *Psychogenic or reactive depressions.*—The main characteristic of these depressions is the exhibition of signs of psychomotor tensional deficiency chiefly in the cortical or dominant right hand, while in the primitive, uneducated left hand there are hardly any vertical alterations. It is not uncommon to observe an inversion of the relationship between the two hands in this plane if the usual character of the subject is hypomanic.

3. Psychopathic Personalities: The M.P.D. in ninety-seven patients whose clinical histories manifested the existence of a psychopathic personality, with a complete absence of actual psychotic signs at the time of examination, are distinguished on the whole by the following characteristics: (*a*) a low value of the coefficients of coherence and constancy or fidelity; (*b*) an increase in the average of the direct deviations in the lineograms which is always greater than one centimeter; (*c*) an imprecision and instability of the movements of the temperamental hand (left) which is, in its turn, dominant in the zigzag, with the exception of the sensible-schizoid personalities (corresponding to those persons colloquially called "small fry"); (*d*) large amplitude of the secondary lineal variations; (*e*) appearance of signs belonging to the cyclothymic or schizothymic constellation; (*f*) a frequency of initial tremors in the right horizontal kinetogram; great average of variation between the length of the model and that of the drawings, especially in the left hand.

4. Congenital Defects (Oligophrenias) and Acquired Defects (Insanities): The chief characteristics of these syndromes is the failure to reproduce the complex forms. The patients lack spatial kinetic

representation and for this reason as soon as they are deprived of visual control they become confused and their movements disorganized, in the measure of the integration required for perfect execution. As a consequence, we see the coarseness and mistiness of the zigzag; the loss of shape of the staircase; and the confusion of the chains which are transformed into a mass of mixed shapes and designs, the irregularity of which sometimes resembles the result of the chronic heredo-degenerative diseases of the central nervous system. Nevertheless in these syndromes the elementary impulse is profoundly disturbed and it has an unmistakable appearance (compare the kinetograms of a general paretic with those of a case of Parkinsonism without notable mental disorder).

5. Organic Psychoses: This term designates the psychoses that result from various inflammatory or destructive processes damaging the integrity of the psychoneuric paths and engender disorganization of mental activity (confusion, dementia). Their termination depends upon the subject's capacity for cerebral recovery, but as long as the destruction continues, there is the more or less characteristic demential syndrome. We observe a widespread and changing phenomenology, in which the obvious disturbance of the logical structure of the mind is prominent as well as the appearance of new psychic creations, a disturbance of the psychomotor activity, and a deep alteration of the autoscopy and corporal schema. For this reason in some cases it is completely impossible for us to obtain the M.P.D., but in many chronic states we are able to obtain the drawings by means of the prevailing tendency to motor automatism (echopraxia). Our clinical material corresponding to these forms is exceedingly poor and it enables us only to state that a mixture of the traits corresponding to the series of schizophrenic processes is observable, as well as of anxiety traits and of phenomena of decortication chiefly visible in the complete lack of control in the lineal kinetograms.

GENERAL DISCUSSION OF THE RESULTS

In summary, after two and a half years of daily clinical investigation, it seems to me that I may continue to sustain the conclusions expressed in my paper to the Royal Society of Medicine (London) as follows:

1) When a subject performs a series of lineal movements in the three basic directions of space according to the technique of the M.P.D., we may expect to obtain data of indubitable interest in the study of his conative trends (reactive attitudes).

2) These data are of two different varieties, quantitative and qualitative, and in accordance with our experience are mutually complementary and significant. The differences existing between the measures concerning one hand and the other serve to point out the degree of intrapersonal cohesion or consistency, i. e., the greater or less confluence between the permanent, fundamental reactive attitudes (constitutional or genotypic) and the temporary and apparent (phenotypic). The former, of a temperamental type, are more apparent in the less-cultivated and less-controlled hand (usually the left) while the latter, of a characterological type, appear in the better-controlled right hand.

3) The data already obtained in the various groups of normal and abnormal patients demonstrate that the average total of the absolute deviations closely expresses the nervous equilibrium of the subject, but the averages of the relative deviations, especially in the sagittal and vertical planes, have a greater psychological significance.

4) We possess sufficient data to convince us that the degree of depression or elation underlying a patient's attitudes can be fully expressed by the sign and quantity of the deviations of his kinetograms in the vertical plane; while the type and value of his aggressiveness can be evaluated through the degree and direction of the deviations in the sagittal plane, the latter providing a good index of the danger of suicide or heteroaggression.

Since formulating these conclusions in England in 1939, I have added the following:

5) While the ascending and descending movements in the vertical plane provide a general notion of the present position of the patient in the *diathetic scale,* and serve to measure the degree of psychomotor tension that can be liberated in the test, the flexor and extensor movements in the sagittal plane (egocifugal advancement or egocipetal recession) suggest to us the relation between the ego and the world, i. e., the direction in which the subject aims his energies. The individuals in whom a predominance of the egocifugal advancement concurs with decreased psychomotor tension are the most inclined to produce the *projection mechanism* characteristic of the paranoid focus. Not in one single case of ideas of persecution has this typical trilogy failed to be present: (*a*) lack of vital energy; (*b*) tendency to introversion; (*c*) compression and potential increase of the aggressiveness. The former is manifested by the descent or fall of the right hand in the vertical kinetogram; the second by the tendency to levogyration; the third by the decisive advance in the sagittal lineogram, perfectly compatible with the possibility of final heaping in the egocifugal zigzag.

6) The prognosis of the course of schizophrenic syndromes after convulsive or insulin treatment may be found in the persistence or absence of schizopraxic signs in the left hand, corresponding to the deeper layers of the personality.

7) After considering the great correlation between the improvement of the myokinetic tracings and the clinical improvement, we may state that a great number of the benefits induced by ergotherapy or occupational treatment stem from the restraint of the defective kinesias (oblique attitudes, stratified impulses in certain centers that withdraw them from the global influence of the cortex in activity) forced by the rhythmical and systematic mobilization of the muscles into new kinetic sequences that absorb or aspirate by negative induction the potential that engenders the psychotic symptoms.

In the same way that a change of position helps the student to gain a new and better focus in his endeavor to study the obscure and tiresome text, a series of changes of position helps the mental patient to obtain a new view of the situations and problems that are worrying him. A great many times we have seen a decrease in the schizopraxic reversions and an improvement in the myokinetic production together with an apparent improvement of the subject's facial expression and dynamism after an hour of manual work.

The myokinetic psychodiagnosis is a convenient, rapid method for detecting among a group of individuals the psychopathic personalities that should be submitted to a careful examination. For this reason, *I believe in its efficacy as a means of civil or military selection.*

It is very easy to detect simulated abnormalities. All that is necessary is to repeat the test after a few minutes to obtain in simulation a coefficient of constancy much too low to be normal. Likewise, it is very difficult for the examinee to effect an improvement of his results through training; but in any case such a possibility can be precluded by the employment of homologous drawings of different sizes.

BIBLIOGRAPHY

(Only the fundamental works consulted or quoted are mentioned.)

Alexander, F. "What Can Psychiatry Contribute to the Alleviation of National and International Difficulties?" a symposium, *Am. Jour. of Orthopsychiatry*, October, 1941.

Ansbacher, H. L. "German Military Psychology," *Psychological Bulletin*, XXXVIII, 370–92, 1941.

Banissoni, F. "Le applicazioni de la Psic. alla selez. e all' instruz. del soldato nei principali paesi," *Arch. Psicol. Neurol. Psichiat. e Psicoterap*, ed. rvd. Fr. Gemelli, I, 379–407, Milano, March, 1940.

Bartlett, F. C. *Psychology and the Soldier*, Cambridge University Press, 1927.

Bingham, W. "The Army Personnel Classification System," *An. Amer. Acad. of Pol. and Soc. Sc.*, Philadelphia, March, 1942.

———. "Psychological Services in the U.S. Army," *Jour. of Consulting Psychol.*, October, 1941.

Faragó, L. *German Psychological Warfare*. New York, New York Committee on National Morale, 1942.

Flinker, R. "Die Psychologie und Psychopathologie der Hysterie," ed. Bostroem and Lange, *Thieme*, XIII, 63, 1938.

Freud, S. *Collected Papers (Civilization, War and Death)*. International Psychoanalytical Library, nos. 7–10. London, Hogarth Press, 1924–1933–1934.

Fribourg-Blanc Rodiet, A. *La folie et la guerre de 1914–1918*. Paris, Alcan, 1930.

Gillespie, R. D. *Psychological Effects of War on Citizen and Soldier*, New York, W. W. Norton & Co., 1942.

Glover, E. *The Psychology of Fear and Courage*. Middlesex, England, Hammondsworth, Penguin Books, 1940.

Goldstein, K. *The Organism, a Holistic Approach to Biology Derived from Pathological Data in Man*, with a foreword by K. S. Lashley,

New York, Cincinnati, etc., American Book Co., 1939. (Essentially a translation of the German original *Der Aufbau des Organismus*.)

Hartwell, S. W. *Presidential Address to American Orthopsychiatric Association* X, 207–15, April, 1940.

Kardiner, A. "The Traumatic Neuroses of War," *Psychosomatic Medicine,* monographs 2–3, 1941.

Miller, E., ed. *The Neuroses in War*. By several authors, with a concluding chapter by H. Crichton Miller. Macmillan Co., 1940.

Mira, E. "Fear," *Lancet,* I, 1935, June 17, 1939.

———. "Myokinetic Psychodiagnosis: New Technique of Exploring the Conative Trends of Personality," *Proceedings of the Royal Soc. of Med.,* London, XXXIII, 173–94, 1940.

———. "Psychiatric Experience in the Spanish War," *British Med. Jour.,* I, 1217–20, June, 1939.

Myers, C. S. *Shell Shock in France 1914–1918*. Based on a war diary kept by Ch. S. Myers. Macmillan Co., 1940.

Overholser, W. "Contributions of Psychiatry to National Defense," *Am. Jour. of Orthopsychiatry,* II, 634–37, October, 1941.

Peixoto, A. "Paranoia" (preliminary study of "collective" delusions). *Rev. de. Psiquiat. y Criminol.,* VI, 393–408 (Spanish version).

Pratt, C. C. *Psychology, the Third Dimension of War*. Columbia Home Front War Books. No. 6. Columbia University Press, 1942.

Rado, Sandor. "The Traumatic Neuroses," *Psychosomatic Medicine,* October, 1942.

Schilder, P. "Differential Diagnosis of Hysterical Tremor," *Arch. of Neur. and Psych.,* XLV, 517–19, March, 1941.

Soldatentum (German journal devoted to military problems. Collection of 1938–41).

INDEX

THE THOMAS WILLIAM SALMON
MEMORIAL LECTURES

The Salmon Lectures of the New York Academy of Medicine were established in 1931, as a memorial to Thomas William Salmon, M.D., and for the advancement of the objects to which his professional career had been wholly devoted.

Dr. Salmon died in 1927, at the age of 51, after a career of extraordinary service in psychiatric practice and education, and in the development of a world-wide movement for the better treatment and prevention of mental disorders, and for the promotion of mental health.

Following his death, a group of his many friends organized a committee for the purpose of establishing one or more memorials that might serve to preserve and pass on to future generations some of the spirit and purpose of his supremely noble and useful life. Five hundred and ninety-six subscriptions were received, three hundred and nineteen from physicians.

Of the amount thus obtained, $100,000 was, on January 10, 1931, given to the New York Academy of Medicine, as a fund to provide an income for the support of an annual series of lectures and for other projects for the advancement of psychiatry and mental hygiene. For the purpose of giving lasting quality to the lectures as a memorial to Dr. Salmon, and of extending their usefulness, it was stipulated that each series should be published in a bound volume of which this volume is one.